THE GUINNESS BOOK OF

robert eastaway

mindbenders

and david wells

GUINNESS PUBLISHING

Cover and page design: Mitchell Associates, Hertford

Illustrations: John Mitchell

This publication © Guinness Publishing Limited (1995),
33 London Road, Enfield, Middlesex

Reprint 10 9 8 7 6 5 4 3 2 1 0

Printed and bound in Great Britain by The Bath Press, Bath

A catalogue record of this book is available from the British Library

ISBN 0-85112-668-5

Acknowledgements

We would like to thank Richard Milbank and Charlotte Howard for their encouragement and excellent powers of persuasion.

Various people have been of enormous help in compiling and testing the material, in particular Janet Pickering, Peter Bloomberg, Helen Nicol and Richard Harris. Special thanks to Richard for contributing so many ideas including those behind numbers 17, 37, and 98. Thanks also to WJE, Matthew Ryan, Michael Haslam, David Flavell, Nick Healey and Tim Jones for their suggestions and improvements to puzzles.

We also owe much to the works of some of the great puzzle composers of the past, including H. E. Dudeney, Kordemsky, Lukac & Tarjan and Lewis Carroll, as well as modern experts such as Martin Gardner and David Singmaster.

The responsibility for any errors that appear in this book, however, is firmly ours.

Foreword

Puzzles should be fun, not a dull slog. For this reason you will find that for many of the mindbenders in this collection you will not need a pencil and paper, just some mental agility. And although there are some very tough ones they usually have neat short cuts.

It is rare to come up with completely original puzzles these days, but we hope that even if you are an expert you will find many here that are completely new to you. The ideas for the puzzles have come from many different sources. A lot of them are based on situations that we have really – well, more or less – encountered. 'Spotting doobreys', 'A borderline case' and 'Cricket for Americans', for example, would fall into this category. In other instances we have added new twists to ideas which are in some cases centuries old.

We have deliberately mixed up the order of the solutions at the back of the book so that when you are looking up the answer to one puzzle you don't by mistake discover the answer to the next one as well. Some of the solutions are quite detailed, and we have included in them – in addition to the 'answers' themselves – a number of interesting or even surprising points that emerge from the puzzles.

Finally, you may like to know that there is a good excuse for spending time on puzzles. Experts agree that one of the most important human skills for the future will be the ability to think creatively. Puzzles – especially those with surprising answers – are a very good way of reminding the brain that it sometimes pays to look at a problem from a different angle, and that crazy notions are sometimes true.

Of course you don't need a serious reason for doing puzzles. We just hope you enjoy them.

Robert Eastaway and David Wells.

The puzzles

The puzzles in this book are not arranged in any particular way. We have mixed up the toughest puzzles with others that you might solve instantly. Number puzzles will be found alongside code-breakers and word games.

We have used the code MB to point out a certain type of really difficult puzzle so that if you are keen on this type you can pick them out more readily. An MB is a real mindbender, one which will definitely require some serious pencil and paper work.

Contents

The Puzzles

1. The alternative nine dots puzzle

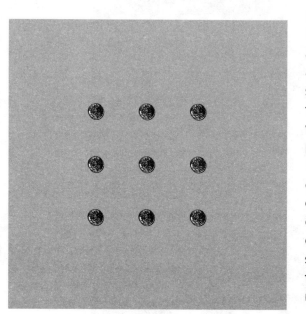

Here are nine coins in a square. No, you aren't going to be asked to draw four straight lines through them without lifting your pen (that one is in *The Guinness Book of Brainteasers*). Your challenge is to move only four coins and end up with a smaller square with three coins in each row and column.

Solution on page 78

2. Cricket for Americans

"Of course love, you Yanks will never understand the English game of cricket," said Brian to Diane, the young American woman who was sitting next to him at the annual cricket club dinner. "I'm from the county of Yorkshire, one of the strongest centres of cricket in the world. Do you know, in the nine summers leading up to the start of the Second World War, Yorkshire won the County Championship seven times?"

"Uhuh, is that right?" said Diane, trying to fake interest. She went on, "Of course now I come to think about it, Yorkshire won in 1931, didn't they? They must have been so pleased after not winning in 1930".

Brian was dumbfounded. "Yes, that's right... I didn't realize you were such an expert... ," he stammered.

"Oh I know absolutely nothing about your crazy English game," replied Diane.

How could Diane be so confident about her guess?

Solution on page 84

Solution on page 84

3. Fun run go slow

This is Angela's first time in the three-mile Fun Run, and she is finding it a little tough. In fact she has only just completed the first two miles, and as she looks at her watch she says to herself (breathlessly), "I'm only averaging four miles an hour. Oh dear, I wanted to average six miles per hour for this run – I must go a bit faster."

How fast will she have to run the final mile in order to get her average speed for the whole Fun Run up to six miles per hour?

Solution on page 88

4. Pam's party

Pam and five of her friends were looking forward to tucking into her birthday cake, which conveniently had six sides, when who should turn up but her cousin, Louise, who of course expected to join in the party and have her share of the cake.

"That's all right," said Pam's mother, "I can divide the cake like this, which makes nine slices, and Daddy and I will have a slice each."

"But we shan't get so much!" complained Pam, "there must be a fair way." Indeed, there was a way to cut the cake into just eight identical pieces, one each for the children and one for Mum and Dad to share.

What was the fair way?

Solution on page 93

5. Christmas card mystery

Last Christmas the Crown & Greyhound pub was selling its own cards. Cards were sold separately and, in theory, you could ask for whatever number of cards you wanted. Among other combinations, many customers bought multiples of 5 cards: a lot bought 5, some bought 15 and a few bought 20. What seems odd, though, is that nobody at all bought ten cards.

Can you think of a simple explanation for this, other than coincidence?

Solution on page 98

6. Typewriter trouble

Dear Mum,

Thanks for sending me your old electronic typewriter. It's great except for a strange little problem with the daisywheel. Every time I type the letter z ju tubsut up hp gvooz. K owuv igv kv hkzhg zlir M gsqi lsqi. Psxw sj pszj. Xzk.

Who sent the letter?

Solution on page 103

7. One 'ell of a puzzle

Jim was a jigsaw puzzle addict. Give him some shapes and he would try to fit them together. "There will be one uncovered square left over!" said his wife, when she saw him trying to fill this square with L-tiles:

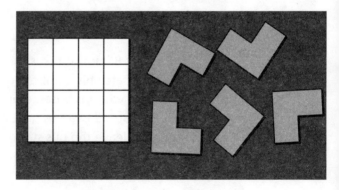

"I know that," said Jim, "that's not the point, the question is where will the uncovered square be?"

Can you discover where the single square which Jim must leave empty after filling the rest of the square with five L-tiles could be?

Solution on page 109

8. Magic beans

"So you don't believe that I can use telepathy to count things?" said Uncle Norman. "OK, pick up any number of beans in your left hand (don't tell me how many!) and pick up the same number in your right hand. Now take four from your left hand and put them in your right hand. Count how many there are remaining in your left hand, put them back in the jar and put the same number from your right hand back in the jar. Now pick five more beans up in your left hand. I can now tell you that you have a total of... " (Uncle Norman concentrated hard) "...13 beans in your hands."

He was right! How did Uncle Norman pull off this amazing bit of psychic counting?

Solution on page 114

9. Missing the bus

Every morning, Mr Blimpton takes the short walk down Acacia Avenue to catch his number 368 bus to work. But there is a problem with his buses, a problem which anybody who has stood in a bus queue will recognize. Even though they leave the bus station every five minutes, by the time they reach his bus stop Mr Blimpton's buses always arrive in threes. (In fact, the buses in his bunches of three are always about thirty seconds apart.)

Now the odd thing is that if Mr Blimpton sees a number 368 bus leaving his bus stop just before he gets there and he misses it, Mr Blimpton actually looks quite pleased. And if he doesn't see a number 368 bus leaving the bus stop, he appears rather more concerned.

Assuming he does actually want to get to work as fast as possible, what could possibly explain the fact that Mr Blimpton seems to prefer missing a bus to not missing one?

Solution on page 120

....

10. Menial copying

"Stephanie, sorry to dump this on you but could you possibly take photocopies of this marketing strategy document, personally deliver one copy to everyone who is coming to my management meeting at noon, and return the original to me?"

"But it's after half past eleven now, Brian."

"Yes I know, I'm sorry to be a pain, must dash."

Stephanie, efficient as ever, did meet the deadline, though conservationists will be disgusted to learn that 371 sheets of paper were churned through the photocopier in this exercise.

How many people do you think went to Brian's meeting?

Solution on page 124

....

11. Turn four into five

It is not difficult to get from TWO to SIX by changing one letter at a time, each time making a proper word, like this:

TWO   TOO   TOP   TIP   SIP   SIX

So TWO to SIX can be done in five steps. FOUR to FIVE takes longer. How many steps do you need to turn

FOUR into FIVE? Can you do it with every letter changing at least once, including the F? How about turning ONE into TWO? And as a final very tough challenge, can you turn SEVEN into EIGHT?
(Our solution has the rare word 'REVET' in the middle.)

Solution on page 78

12. Can you do it?

You have a cylindrical can of the sort that baked beans are sold in. You want to fill it exactly one quarter full of water, but you have no measuring instrument and the can is not graduated in any way (though you can scratch it yourself if you wish).

How should you proceed?

Solution on page 84

13. Less or fewer

For several years the British supermarket chain Sainsbury annoyed many people by having a sign above one of the express checkout tills in each store which read 'Eight items or less'. Purists said that this should have read 'Eight items or **fewer**'. The use of less and fewer confuses many people. Perhaps you can sort this out. Look at this sentence and count the number of f's:

> 'THE FIGHTING FORCES THAT ARE SAFELY STATIONED SOUTH OF THE BORDER ARE SHORT OF MOTOR FUEL.'

Would it be right to say that there are fewer than six f's in that sentence, or that there are less than six f's?

Solution on page 88

14. Fair prizes

Four girls at the back of the classroom were comparing the number of prizes they had won at the fair. "I've got one more than you," said Bernice. "I've got two more than you," said one girl to another. "I've got three more than you" said one to another, "I've got four more than you", "I've got five more than you", "I've got six more than you", rang out their excited voices, but we don't know who was talking to whom.

If they won a total of 27 prizes, how many did Bernice win?

Solution on page 93

15. Mrs Bearskin's quilt

On the left is a quilt which Mrs Bearskin has had for years.

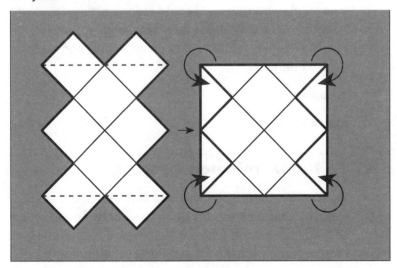

Originally it was made from eight small squares sewn together. Now Mrs Bearskin is tired of the floppy shape and plans to cut it up and re-sew it as in the diagram on the right, to make a square quilt.

However, she is not satisfied with having to cut out five pieces, and she is not very struck by the new design either. Can you help her do it in four pieces?

Solution on page 98

16. A borderline case

"How long is the boundary between Spain and Portugal?" asked Pamela, innocently.

"According to the Spanish map we used last holiday, it's 987 kilometres," replied her father. "But the Portuguese customs man disagreed," added her mother, "he said it was 1214 kilometres long."

"I think they're both wrong," said Pamela, "I think that with my little ruler," – at this point she waved her school ruler in the air – "I could measure it exactly, and it would be exactly 2000 kilometres long!" "Don't be silly," her father replied. "Get on with your homework," said her mother.

Who was right?

Solution on page 103

17. Not Mornington Crescent

The London Underground is not only one of the great tourist features of the city, it has also become the source of many games and puzzles. Here is one little riddle that requires absolutely no knowledge of the underground.

There is a certain feature we have in mind, and only two stations have it.

Oxford Circus, for example, doesn't have this feature. Nor does Tottenham Court Road, nor Mornington Crescent. But Mansion House does have it (with a bit to spare), and South Ealing is the only station that has it precisely!

What is the special feature we have in mind?

Solution on page 110

18. Extended intervals

The following announcement was once heard by passengers waiting for a train on the London Underground: "We apologize for the extended intervals between trains, due to a delay early this morning."

What was wrong with this excuse?

Solution on page 115

19. Tunnel wires

Digging of the controversial tunnel under the River Sploog has just been completed, and engineer Bob Truffles has laid four electric cables along the tunnel. Unfortunately the four cables look absolutely identical, and there are so many twists and turns in them that it is now impossible to tell which is which. Bob could walk through the tunnel untwisting the cables, but he has thought of a better way of sorting them out: his plan is to join two cables together at one end of the tunnel,

starting with A and B, and then at the other end see which two cables make a complete electrical circuit when he puts power through them. The first test he does will obviously only tell him that two cables are either 'A and B' or 'B and A'.

Using this method, how many trips along the tunnel does he need to make in order to label all four cables correctly?

Solution on page 120

. . . .

20. The tall and the short of it

"At eeeeeeease!" yelled the sergeant, and the nine squaddies stood at ease in their usual square formation. "You wanted to speak to the men, SIR!" he yelled at the lieutenant standing next to him.

"Yes, thank you Sergeant. Actually, all I want you to do is to select the shortest man in each row, and when you have done that, tell the tallest one of the shortest men to come and see me at 12 noon."

"Right you are, SIR," he replied, and started to mutter to himself, "the tallest of the shortest in each row, the shortest of the tallest in each row, or was it column, the shortest of the tallest in each column, damn, which was it, oh, it doesn't matter, it won't make any difference anyway..." He went ahead and selected the tallest man in each column and selected the shortest of these three.

Did this decision make a difference?

Solution on page 125

....

21. A knotty poser

John bought a piece of wood two metres square from the local DIY store. He wanted to cut the wood into

four identical two-metre long planks that were as wide as possible. Unfortunately, when he got to look at the wood closely, he found it contained a circular knot which was four centimetres in diameter. Clearly he would have to cut the wood into narrower planks, and throw away the piece with the knot in it.

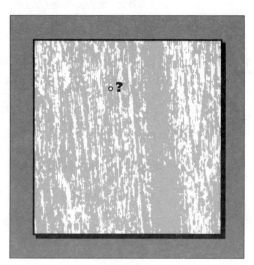

Even more unluckily, the knot was in the worst possible position, and when John cut his four planks he had no choice but to waste more than one fifth of his wood.

Where was the knot situated?

Solution on page 79

....

22. Elementary?

"Watson, I want to demonstrate one of the fundamental principles of deduction. Mrs Hudson, would you join us please. I have three handkerchiefs here: two of them are white, one is blue. Now both of you shut your eyes while I put one handkerchief on each of your heads. I will hide the third handkerchief so you don't know which one it is. Then I want you to deduce which colour is on your head." Mrs Hudson and Dr Watson did as they were told.

"Right, Mrs Hudson, open your eyes. Can you tell me which handkerchief is on your head?"

She shook her head.

"Well now, Watson, from what Mrs Hudson said, I'm sure you can tell me your colour?"

"But she didn't say anything, Holmes."

"Exactly."

What colour was Watson wearing?

Solution on page 85

....

23. Shorter circuit

The M964 motorway around the city of Climthorpe is a circle with three lanes running in each direction. Police Constable Grommet was told he would be responsible for patrolling it next week and he decided to drive around it to get to know it better. First, he did a circuit clockwise, always driving in the slow lane. Then he did a circuit anticlockwise in the slow lane. But he noticed from his accurate mileometer that one of his journeys was shorter than the other one.

Which journey was shorter, and by roughly how much?

Solution on page 88

24. An Olympic effort

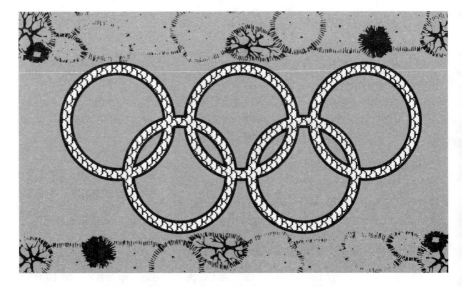

The concrete paths around the flower beds in Daniel's local park are in the shape of the Olympic rings. Daniel managed to cycle along every stretch of path without doing any stretch twice and without crossing his own tracks or leaving the path. How did he do it?

Solution on page 94

25. Inverted clock

For his birthday Tom was given a square clock resembling a school easel, with a blank face on which he could chalk the numbers himself. When he took the clock out of the box he accidentally had the face upside down, so that when he came to chalk on the numbers he put them in the opposite position to where they should have been: 12 went where 6 should be, for example, and 3 where 9 should be. He put in the

batteries and then tried to move the hands round to show the right time.

Would he be able to spot that anything was wrong?

Solution on page 99

....

26. Do you get the picture?

Three millionaire art collectors were boasting about their latest transactions. "Last week I sold my 'Study of Black on Black' to Fred here," said Nigel, "and it improved the average value of my collection and his collection at the same time! Neat, huh?"

"It's true," said Fred, "and, what is more, the next day I sold my painting 'Three Bananas and a Grapefruit' to Percy, didn't I, Percy," here he turned to the third portly figure, "and once again the average value of both our collections was raised."

"So the average values of all our collections have gone up," said Nigel. "Seems like something for nothing to me."

"Wonderful!" cried Fred and Percy in unison.

How is it possible for the average values to have gone up for everyone? Or is this just another city wheeze?

Solution on page 103

27. Fast food

Pete's Pizza Pantry has been a rip-roaring success so far. "We pride ourselves on our amazingly speedy service," says Pete, who likes to take a stopwatch to his hard-working staff as they slave over the grills. He started off with three pizza makers, who could produce, in total, three pizzas in three minutes. Now business is booming and he's doubling his staff to six pizza makers.

How long will it take them to produce six pizzas?

Solution on page 110

28. Lucky friends

"The aunt of one of my classmates won £500 in the National Lottery," said David at supper that evening. "Well somebody at our school's family won £1000," added his sister. "What a coincidence," said their father, "one of my friends at work was telling me the other day that a friend of his had had a decent win." "Gosh, we do know some lucky people don't we – it seems that everyone is lucky except for us," observed their mother.

How do you account for them having so many lucky friends?

Solution on page 115

29. Is this the world's simplest game?

This game is so simple that when a group of primary school pupils were shown it a while ago, they quickly discovered the winning strategy and then decided that it was no longer worth playing. Can you do the same?

25

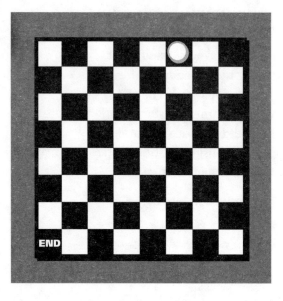

The rules are extremely simple. The single piece is placed somewhere on the board, and then the two players take it in turns to move it from the square it is on to any new square, as long as they move it in a straight line parallel to the sides of the board (in other words, like a rook in chess). Every move, however, must be either down the board, towards the bottom edge, or leftwards, towards the left-hand edge. The winning player is the one who makes the final move onto the square marked END.

We show a typical starting position. It is your turn to play. What move do you play to make your opponent squirm?

Solution on page 121

30. Pub quiz

Every year the pubs in Gussetshire hold a knockout quiz tournament. The rules are that three teams take part in each contest, and only the winning team gets through to the next round. Usually, there are some byes in the first round (which means some teams get through without having to take part in a contest).

The final this year was very tense, and everything hung

on the last question. The three teams sat with fingers on the buzzers when the questionmaster asked the following poser: "37 teams entered this tournament this year. How many contests have there been?"

What was the winning answer?

Solution on page 125

31. Interesting words

"I hope this doesn't sound facetious," said Edward as he and his Spanish friend Carlos stood outside Harrods waiting for the sale to start, "but one of the great strengths of my country is our patience when queueing." In so saying, he neatly squeezed into one sentence three words whose combinations of letters make them special.

Which ones are they and why are they special?

Solution on page 79

32. Dawdling home

"Oh, stop dawdling," cried Jane, as James stopped to look in another shop window, "I want to catch the bus!" "It doesn't make any difference how much we dawdle," replied James, "since we have not the slightest idea when the bus is coming, we can expect to wait the same time on average, however long we take to get to the stop."

"Oh, don't be silly," said Jane, "I want to get home as soon as possible, of course we ought to hurry."

Who is right, Jane or James?

Solution on page 85

33. Screw on your thinking cap!

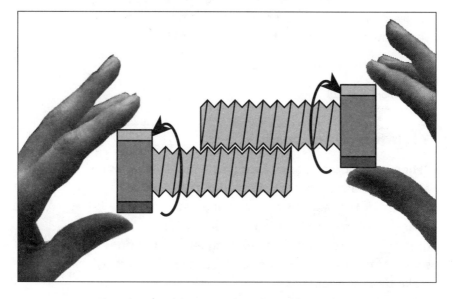

The picture shows one hand, on the right, turning a bolt in a clockwise direction, as if screwing it into a nut, and another hand, on the left, turning another screw anticlockwise, as if unscrewing it.

As it happens, the two bolts are in close contact all the time, so they will either be drawn closer together, or will be pushed further apart, or perhaps they won't move closer or further apart.

Without using a pair of bolts to experiment with, can you predict the correct answer?

Solution on page 89

34. True or false

In the box opposite, which of the statements is true, and which is false?

1. The number of false statements in this box is one.

2. The number of false statements in this box is two.

3. The number of false statements in this box is three.

4. The number of false statements in this box is four.

Solution on page 95

35. Spotting doobreys

Edward Spinks is a keen bird-watcher, so last week he was particularly excited to discover that a pair of lesser wattled doobreys were nesting in the tree at the back of his garden. He has set up a hide in his back room, and every evening when he returns from work he sits down to study the birds.

He has observed that the doobreys have young chicks, and that, in order to feed them, the male and female are on a non-stop food search. The two parents work separately, flying off over the hedge, returning about 15 minutes later with grub (literally) and then within seconds flying off again on their next search.

But there is something that Edward cannot explain. The first bird he sees each day is sometimes the male and sometimes the female. But the first sighting is always of a bird flying back to the nest, rather than leaving the nest. Even when he gets home early, he still doesn't see a doobrey leave the nest until he has seen one fly back.

Can you think of the most likely explanation for this interesting ornithological phenomenon?

Solution on page 100

36. Mustafa square

Mustafa has discovered that if you multiply five by itself, the result ends in five. He has found this is also true for six (which results in 36). And it also works for 25 (625) and 76 (5776), and for 625 and 376. It seems to him that for any number of digits there are always just two numbers that work.

But Mustafa is then surprised to discover that there is only one four figure number which, when squared, ends in itself. Can you find it? And can you explain why there isn't a second one?

(Mustafa has ignored zero and one which also work, of course.)

Solution on page 104

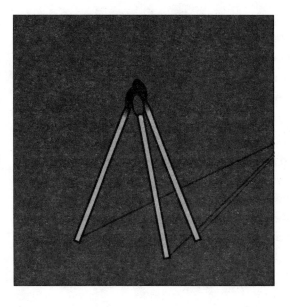

Solution on page 104

37. Match this...

Rachel welded two matches together by setting light to the heads. Then she leant a third match against the pair to form a little tripod. Even though the third match was still loose, she found that using one unburnt match she could lift the whole tripod safely into the air. She didn't touch the tripod with anything except the fourth match, nor did she weld the fourth match to the tripod.

How did she do it?

Solution on page 110

38. A minor case

Sherlock Holmes was investigating what appeared to be a very minor break-in, as a favour to a friend. "Even you, my dear Watson," he began, "can solve this case by attentively observing the rather scuffed footprints that proceed through the scullery door, and along the hall, and disappear into the room on the left. What do you see?"

"Er, they're muddy?" ventured Watson. "Think logically, Watson!" urged Holmes. "They proceed right foot, right foot, left foot, left foot, right, right, left, left and so on. What do you see now?"

At last he understood. What had Watson realized?

Solution on page 115

39. Lord Henry's hunt

The fox-hunters were gathering outside the Red Lion. It was a hot sticky day and several of the hounds were lying on the ground having a doze before the off. Lord Henry was getting changed while planning the after-hunt celebrations with his butler, Basil. "Oh, by the way – pack my box with five dozen liquor jugs," ordered Henry. Then suddenly, out of the blue, a creature shot out of the bushes and bolted off down the road. "Excuse me," said Basil, "but did you see that? A quick brown fox jumped over that lazy dog!" "Action stations!" yelled Henry. "Quick Baz, get my woven flax jodhpurs!" Basil fetched the special trousers, Henry squeezed himself in to them, and with a call of "Tally ho!" led the hunt off into the neighbouring field.

Meanwhile, did you notice more than one interesting feature in what they said?

Solution on page 121

....

40. Tricky ending

Using only one word, and correct grammar, complete the following sentence as accurately as you can:

'The number of occurrences of the number one in this sentence is...'

Solution on page 126

....

41. Safe cracking

In order to gain entry to a safe belonging to the infamous miser Frugal McDougall you need to find the code. The code is a ten-digit number which uses every digit between 0 and 9.

Frugal always leaves his code on the front of the safe, but he disguises it in a particular way. He writes the first five digits along the top of a 5 x 5 grid, and the last five digits down the side. Then he multiplies each digit along the top by each digit down the side, and thus fills up the grid with 25 numbers. Finally he erases his code number from the top and side so that only the grid remains.

Unfortunately, on this occasion, not only has he erased his code, he has also erased most of the numbers in the grid. And of the remainder, several digits are so hard to read that we have replaced them with a question mark (For example, the code's third digit multiplied by its ninth digit is 'twenty-something'.)

Can you crack this safe?

Solution on page 80

42. Pencils ready!

Can you draw this shape without taking your pencil off the paper and without drawing any line twice?

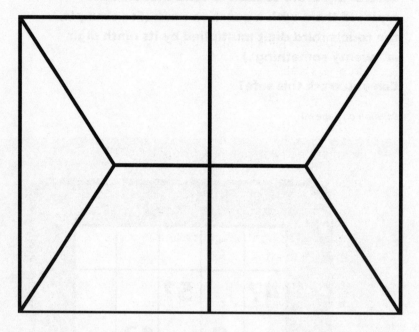

No, you can't. But then, that's not the question. The real puzzle is to decide the minimum amount to be rubbed out so that the figure remaining can be drawn without taking your pencil off the paper. What would you delete?

Solution on page 86

43. Faulty scoring

The scene is Ribblesfield Tennis Club, it's the final of the club championship, and John Tuttle and Bill Hemp are involved in a nail-biting game of singles. The electronic scoreboard shows the score at five games all. Tuttle prepares to serve:

> [Sound effect] Pok pok pok
>
> Umpire: 15-love
>
> [Sound effect] Pok pok pok pok
>
> Umpire: 15-all
>
> [Sound effect] Pok
>
> Umpire: 30-15
>
> [Sound effect] Pok pok pok pok pok OUT!!!
>
> Umpire: Deuce.
>
> Tuttle: Umpire, you must be joking.
>
> Hemp: Tuttle's right. Everyone knows deuce doesn't come after 30-15!
>
> Umpire: Sorry, I know it's unusual but let's leave it at deuce anyway, it's a bit hard to adjust the scoreboard now – unless you want to start this service game again.

After a heated discussion the players finally concede that it is quite fair for the umpire to leave the score at deuce, whereas starting the game again would give Tuttle an unfair advantage.

How do you explain the umpire's decision?

Solution on page 89

....

44. A six pack

Fitting four words into a word square is not difficult. But can you fit more than four words into a

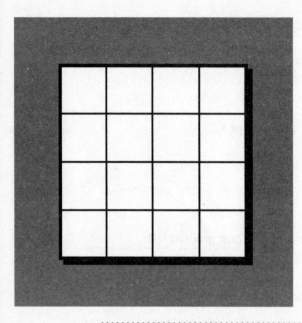

4 x 4 word square?

For example, can you fit these six words into the square: AREA, REAR, DEED, DART, BRAT, BARD?

Solution on page 95

45. Christmas birthdays

At a family gathering over Christmas, Mr Hethrington commented:

"Something strange seems to be happening to our family's birthdays. Have you noticed how New Year's Day comes exactly one week after Christmas Day? Yet the year Mum was born, Christmas was on a Tuesday and New Year was on a Monday. What's more, two days ago Damien was eight years old, yet next year he will be 11. And Janet seems to be extremely lucky. Even though she was also born soon after Christmas, her birthday is always in the middle of summer."

What date is it, and how do you explain the strange birthdays?

Solution on page 100

46. Ring in the ring road

The town of Slowcrawly has such a volume of traffic that – at vast expense – it has just built a new ring road, which is divided into four parts by the two main roads passing through the town. These roads are straight and cross at right angles.

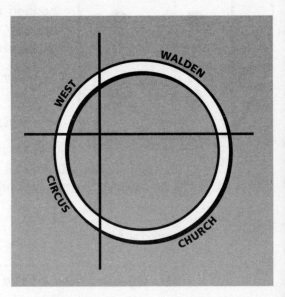

The four parts of the ring road have been given names, as you can see, and your poser is to say, without any complicated measuring, whether the total length of West Street and Church Street, is greater or less than the total length of Walden Road and The Circus.

Solution on page 105

47. Test your mental vision

On the table in front of you is a die, with the four spots facing you and six on top.

Idly passing the time, you tip it one turn away from you (so six is at the back) and then once to the right (so four is now on the right), then once towards you and once to the left. To your surprise you notice that it has not returned to its original position, although you have tipped it once forwards and once back and once to the

right and once to the left.

The question is – if you repeat this same sequence of moves, once each – forwards, right, backwards, left – will it ever return to its original position, and if so, after how many moves? Can you work it out without experimenting with a die?

Solution on page 111

....

48. Polar bearings

You are travelling to the North Pole by sled, but your huskies are too enthusiastic and you overshoot the Pole slightly. Will east be to your left or right?

Solution on page 116

....

49. By-election blues

"What can you tell me about our party's potential candidates for the by-election, Peter?" asked Humphrey Dimpsworth, the local party chairman, counting up the number on the list.

"Well, I have good news and bad news. The good news is that I've had some research done to see if they meet our usual criteria, and we've discovered that eight of them are happily married at the moment, seven of them were not involved in that council scandal four years ago, and six of them have never been involved in any lunatic fringe activities."

"Excellent, let's see, that means at very minimum one of the candidates must have all three of these virtues. What's the bad news?"

"Er, well, you're right, but unfortunately there is only one candidate who has all three virtues – and it is your old sparring partner Henrietta Prigg."

How many candidates were there in total?

Solution on page 122

. . . .

50. Mate in one

Peter was watching his two brothers playing a game of chess. At one point in the game, Peter sketched out exactly what he saw on the board, and his diagram is shown here. The interesting thing is that it was his eldest brother David's move next (he was playing with the

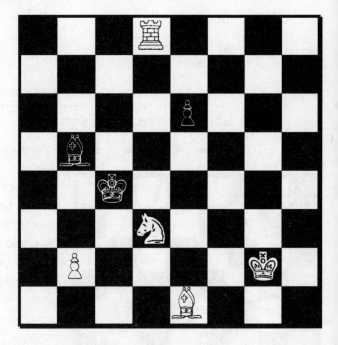

white pieces), and he achieved checkmate that move.

What was David's move?

Solution on page 126

51. Scattered vegetables

There is a logical reason why one of vegetables listed below is the most appropriate to insert in the following sentence. Can you say which?

"I do not like those people leaving _____ scattered everywhere."

(a) sprouts

(b) beans

(c) potatoes

(d) swedes

(e) carrots

Solution on page 80

52. The vanishing square

Below is a diagram of an ordinary chessboard. As you can

see, it has already been cut into four pieces, A, B, C, and D. Now, the interesting thing is that A, B, C and D can be rearranged into a rectangle in the pattern shown on page 41. The number of squares on the original chessboard was 64. In the new rectangle, which has 13 squares across and five squares down, there are 65 squares.

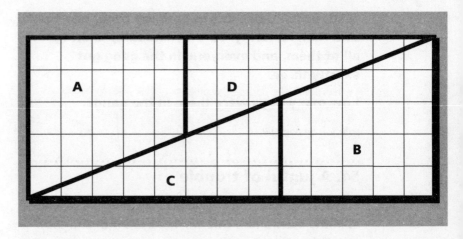

Where has the new square come from? And is it white or black?

Solution on page 86

. . . .

53. Fair shares for all

"I'll keep one sweet for myself, then we'll have exactly the right number in order to split the rest between us equally," said Alan to the other three boys, putting one sweet into his pocket. But at that moment Ed arrived to demand his fair share.

"In that case," said Alan, putting another sweet in his pocket, "now we can share equally between the five of us," but before they could do so, Fergus and Graham turned up. "Oh well," muttered Alan, taking one back from his pocket, "now we can still share equally."

"Oh, no you can't," said Barry, as the rest of the gang appeared over the hill and flung their bikes on the grass.

"I suppose I'd better put back my other one too," said Alan forlornly. So they ended up sharing all of them, and everyone in the gang got exactly three.

How many boys were there in the gang?

Solution on page 90

....

54. A jugful of trouble

You are in possession of two plain cylindrical containers, as in the illustration. One will hold 11 pints, and the other seven pints.

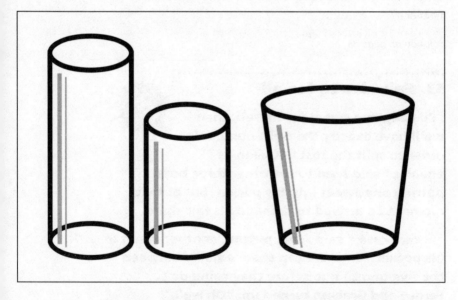

To start with they are both empty, but you have an endless supply of water from a tap.

How can you leave 27 pints in the bowl on the right, in just four moves?

Solution on page 95

55. A weighty problem

Nine identical-looking parcels, each containing one of Mr Wentlesprocket's new scalp-massaging inventions, had been loaded onto the train. The train was ready to depart when the frantic Wentlesprocket came running along the platform.

"Hold the train," he yelled, "one of my devices is missing its fringe-equalizer. Without it the whole thing might melt when the customer tries to use it."

"Well you'd better find it quick, we leave in two minutes," said the guard.

There was no time to unwrap the packages, but Wentlesprocket had brought with him a set of scales which would allow him to compare the weights of parcels against each other. The parcel that was slightly lighter would be the one without the fringe-equalizer. Unfortunately there was only time for two weighings.

How could Wentlesprocket be sure he found the right parcel?

Solution on page 100

56. Superball rebound

Craig has a superball – so super that when you drop it, it bounces right back to the height you dropped it from. He's wondering what would happen if he threw the ball at something moving. Let's suppose he was standing on a railway line and a diesel train was bearing down on him at 50 miles per hour.

He then threw the superball at 20 miles per hour straight at the oncoming train. When the ball bounced off the front of the train, how fast would the ball be travelling towards Craig?

Solution on page 106

. . . .

57. A noticeable problem

Ravioli al Sugo, the notorious spy, was waiting for a train on a platform at Victoria Station when he noticed

by glancing below the large vertical sign saying 'VICTORIA', a person whom he suspected was Inspector Grabber of the Yard.

We say 'suspected' because Ravioli could only see the man up to the knot of his tie, his head being hidden behind the notice. Ravioli's first impulse was to walk smartly away, on the grounds that if he could see enough of Inspector Grabber to recognize him, Grabber would be able to see enough of Ravioli to recognize him – but then he stopped and decided to stay in the same place.

Why did Ravioli change his mind?

Solution on page 111

58. The key question

The room keys at the Netherhampton hotel are kept on a set of hooks as shown in the diagram.

Harold the concierge is about to return the keys to

the set (one key per hook) when he has a strange thought. If he hangs keys on hooks 1 and 3 then there is a hook (2) which is exactly midway between the two with keys on them. Likewise if he hangs keys on 5 and 11 there is a hook midway

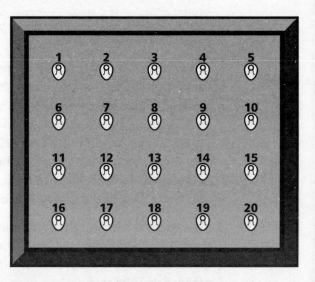

between them (8). But he can hang three keys on 1, 6 and 9 and none of the midpoints between them is a hook.

Harold wonders what is the biggest number of keys he can hang so that no two hooks with keys on have a hook midway between them?

Solution on page116

59. Mum's secret

"How old are you, Mum?"

"I'm 35."

"But you've been 35 for years."

"Yes, but this time it's true. I'm just ignoring the weekends."

How old is Mum?

Solution on page 123

60. Switching olives

Tim's mother has meticulously sorted the nibbles for tonight's party so that there are 100 black olives in the black dish, and 100 green olives in the green dish. They look beautiful but Tim thinks the display boring, so, unknown to his mother, he takes 20 green olives and puts them in the black dish. Then he mixes up the olives in the black dish and takes 20 from this mixture and puts them back in the green olive dish.

His mother is furious. "Now I'm going to have to sort them out. I don't know whether there are more green olives in the black dish, or black olives in the green dish," she says.

Can you help?

Solution on page 126

61. Baywatch

Wayne is a lifeguard on a Californian beach. A man in the sea is shouting for help, and Wayne is ready to leap into action. Wayne can run in the thick sand at six metres per second and can swim at two metres per second, and he wants to reach the stranded man as fast as possible, not least because he is being watched by ten adoring West Coast babes.

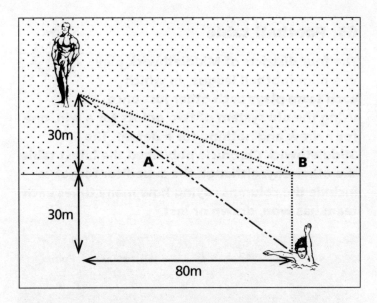

Which is the best route for him: should he aim straight for the man but do a lot of swimming (route A) or minimize the swimming distance but go further by taking route B? Can you find a better route than A or B?

Solution on page 81

62. Pyramid puzzle

The famous archaeologist Professor von Spitzbender was looking at some interesting old carvings on a cave wall. "Mmm, zis appears to be a diagram of a pyramid," he said. "Let me study it through my magnifying glass."

The magnifying glass makes all of the sides of the pyramid appear twice as long. "Aha, zis corner of ze pyramid appears to be exactly 60 degrees," said the Professor. What was the angle of the corner before magnification?

Solution on page 87

63. Football table

The four districts of Middlethwick play
in a mini-football league, in which
each team plays each other just once,
using the old system of two points for a win, one
for a draw and nothing for a defeat. The
Middlethwick Chronicle published the latest table
the other day, although the subeditor forgot to
include the columns saying how many times each
team has won, drawn or lost.

	Goals for	Goals against	Points
Chinfield	2	1	4
Argleford	3	2	3
Dippleton	1	1	2
Bimpley	0	2	1

The question is simple, but the answer is tricky:
have Dippleton played Bimpley yet and, if so,
what was the score?

Solution on page 90

64. T for two

The following riddle was given to two men:

*The letter 't' appears many times in this little riddle and
also appears in the answer. The question is, exactly how
many times in total does 't' appear in this question and
in its answer?*

Each of the men wrote down the answer using words, as opposed to numbers, each of them was right, and yet their answers differed by one.

What were their answers?

Solution on page 96

65. A dicey cube

Mark has made a cube at school, and drawn some numbers on the faces. Here are three views of the cube. As you can see, one of the views only shows one face front on, the number one.

What number is on the opposite face to four on the cube?

Solution on page 100

66. Leave and let die

"So Missterrr Bond, now zat I haf shown you how I plan to take over ze vurld, it is time for me to put you to a slow and agonizing death. I haf stripped you of your shirt and tied you so you cannot move. I am going to seal you into zis airtight chamber, vith barely enough room to sving a cat. It is so vell insulated zat no heat can enter or leave it. In ze chamber you vill notice I have left a large kitchen freezer svitched on at full power – and vith ze door jammed open! Already zis chamber is at only five degrees centigrade. Goodbye and say your prayers... Mr Bond."

How long do you think that James has to manufacture his escape before he freezes to death: minutes, hours or days?

Solution on page 106

67. Midnight mayhem

At Miss Frobisher's Academy for Young Ladies the girls all sleep in dormitories around a quadrangle. There are six beds in each dorm, but, as you can see, pupil numbers are rather low at the moment:

Each night, the matron Mrs Battelax, not exactly the brightest of souls, checks on the number of girls by counting up the totals in each of the outside rows. At present these are 8–10–8–6, counting clockwise from the bottom left corner as shown.

This particular evening, soon after lights out, and after the numbers had been checked in the usual way, four girls slipped into adjacent dorms to join their neighbours for poker. An hour later, another four girls slipped into adjacent dorms, this time for a midnight drink.

An hour later still, Mrs Battelax did her rounds, and wrote down the total number of girls in each row in

her book: they were
6–8–10–8. The reverse of
normal! She was thinking
that perhaps she had gone
round in the wrong
direction, when she
suddenly realized the real
problem: one of the dorms
had been completely empty.

Your poser is to state
which dorm now was
now empty.

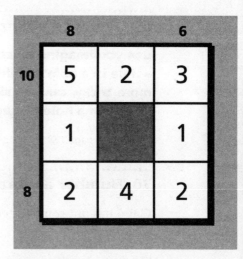

Solution on page 112

68. Twin tea bags

Bill stores tea bags in a jar. The type of tea bag he uses
comes joined in pairs. Every morning he makes himself a
cuppa. Sometimes he reaches into the jar and finds he
has pulled out a double tea bag, in which case he tears
one off for his mug and throws the other back in the
jar. Other times he pulls out a single one, in which case
he just pops it in his mug. And when the jar is empty he
fills it up with another box of 40.

Bill has just returned from holiday and can't remember
how full the tea bag jar is. He is about to reach into the
jar when he says to himself: "Hmm... am I more likely to
pull out a single tea bag or a double tea bag? Since
double tea bags are twice as big as singles, I'm more
likely to pull out a double."

Is he right? Or is he more likely to pick out a single?

Solution on page 117

69. A holey poser

Can you imagine what 'a hole through a hole in a hole' would look like? Even more tricky, can you sketch a picture of 'a hole in a hole through a hole in a hole?'

Solution on page 123

70. Number anagram

Claire has put some letter blocks together to make the following sum:

O N E + T W E L V E = T H I R T E E N

Nicola uses all these blocks but rearranges some of them to get a different sum, which is also correct. Then Claire replaces the 'I' with another 'E' and inserts another '+' block. She rearranges the blocks again and once more the result is correct.

Can you find the two new versions?

Solution on page 127

71. Pointed stars

Here is a seven-pointed star with a perfect heptagon inside it (all its sides are the same length). It was drawn using seven strokes of the pen and without the pen leaving the paper. Using the same number of strokes of the pen and without your pen leaving the paper, can

you create a
shape which has
the silhouette of
a **six**-pointed star
and which has as
its inside shape a
hexagon (which
need not be
perfect)?

Solution on page 81

72. T-shirt teaser

Scruffy Sam has put on his T-shirt. Unfortunately it is
inside out and back to front. Normally the washing
label is on the inside of the left sleeve. Where is it now?

Solution on page 87

73. Secret number club

On his first day at college, maths student Derek found
this curious note in his pigeonhole:

> *Dear Derek*
>
> *I belong to a secret code club. As one of
> my fellow members recently said, each
> of us has a special whole number
> (between 6 and 9) and before we write
> down any number we always add our
> own special number to it. There are 10
> members in the club, and there are 6
> others who have a smaller number than*

me. All of our special numbers add up to
27. If you can tell me what my special
number is, you can join the club.

Yours

Archie Meades

Derek was convinced that there was a mistake, but he was wrong. Can you help him?

Solution on page 91

....

74. Mirror writing

THIS PARAGRAPH CONTAINS A SPECIAL WORD. IF YOU TURN THE PARAGRAPH UPSIDE DOWN AND LOOK AT IT IN A MIRROR, THE SPECIAL WORD WILL MIRACULOUSLY BECOME DECODED WHILE EVERY SINGLE OTHER WORD WILL HAVE BEEN SLIGHTLY MESSED UP. CAN YOU FIND THE SPECIAL WORD (WITHOUT USING A MIRROR)?

Solution on page 96

....

75. He who hesitates is lost

Mr Pendlebury was both indecisive and impatient. Having waited alone at his usual bus stop for what seemed like ages, with no bus in sight, he finally decided to walk to the next bus stop, which he could see, and hope that he got there before the bus.

What happened? Stepping out briskly, and glancing repeatedly over his shoulder, he had only gone 100 metres or so when he spotted the bus coming in the distance, travelling three times as fast as he could run. He looked at the bus stop he had come from, then at the next one. On a quick calculation, he could sprint to either

54

stop and arrive just as the bus got there. Indecision gripped him. He moved from one foot to the other, changed his mind again, and the bus went sailing by.

How far was Mr Pendlebury from the second bus stop when he spotted the bus?

Solution on page 101

76. Card money

Four men decided to spend an evening playing bridge for money. To make it fair, they would play three matches (or 'rubbers') so that they each partnered each other once. They agreed that after each match, the losers would each pay one penny to the winners for every point that the winners made. In the three matches, the winners scored 900, 1000 and 1100 points. One of the players ended the evening £10 better off.

How did the other three get on?

Solution on page 107

77. A classic stick trick

How many matches need to be moved to make a perfect square with these four matches?

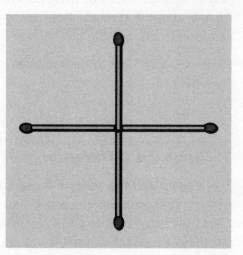

Solution on page 112

78. Surprise meal

"Darling, I've seen so little of you recently that one evening this week I am going to take you out for a meal, but the evening I choose will be a surprise," said Andrew on Monday morning. "That would be nice," said Jenny, who immediately tried to work out which night Andrew would choose.

"Well, it can't be Friday," she thought, "because if by the time we get to Friday morning we haven't been out I'll know it must be that evening, so it won't be a surprise. But since it can't be Friday, then that means it can't be Thursday either, because on Thursday morning I'll know it's going to have to be on Thursday evening. But then that means it can't be Wednesday because it isn't on Thursday or Friday... and it can't be Tuesday... or tonight... he's not going to take me out for a surprise meal at all, the lying so-and-so. How typical!" Her logic seemed impeccable.

But when she got back to the flat that evening there was a message on the answerphone from Andrew: "Jenny, about that meal – how about going to the Tandoori restaurant tonight?"

Jenny was surprised. What had been wrong with her reasoning?

Solution on page 117

79. Spot the difference

The leopard and the cheetah wanted to find out which of them could run the quickest. "That little stream is 100 paces away, I'll race you to it," said the cheetah. Off they ran, and the cheetah was ten paces ahead of

the leopard when she sprang over the stream. "I'm too fast for you," said the cheetah. "I tell you what, let's do that race again, but this time you start from the same place, and I will start ten paces behind you."
The leopard agreed, and they ran the race again at exactly the same speeds.

Who won this time?

Solution on page 123

80. Set in order

Mr Knowall's children have been using his favourite set of encyclopedias for their homework research, but as usual they have not bothered to put them back in the correct order. In fact, they are horribly jumbled.

Mr Knowall wants to put them back in order, but naturally, because each volume is very heavy, he wants to remove from the shelf as few volumes as possible. One move consists of taking a volume off the shelf, pushing some of the remaining books to one side and replacing the volume he took off.

What is the smallest number of moves needed to put the books in order?

Solution on page 127

81. The glass that cheers

It was time for the Christmas punch to be handed round, a sociable activity that Scrooge loathed, so every year he put it off for as long as possible. This year he devised a tricky puzzle using all the punch glasses to offer his guests.

"Before we dip into the bowl," he said to his assembled guests, "I invite you to solve this puzzle. You have to turn all the glasses the right way up, by inverting three at a time. When you invert three glasses, that counts as one move. And you must do it in the smallest number of moves possible. How many? Eh?"

How could his guests get their punch?

Solution on page 82

82. Pardon me, boys

Mike and Merv work as shoe-shiners outside the railway station. To shine the shoes, they first apply the polish (which takes one minute) and then they rub it up to a shine (which takes three minutes). The last train leaves in just under eight minutes and they are about to pack in for the day when three customers arrive.

Can Mike and Merv shine the shoes and still both catch the train?

Solution on page 87

83. Old MacDonald

Old MacDonald had a farm. And on that farm he had...

One animal with half as many letters now as it had when it was younger.

One animal with fewer letters now than it will have when it is older.

One animal with half as many letters as its plural.

One animal with the same number of letters as its plural.

And altogether they had E-I-E-I-O (though not in that order). What were the animals?

Solution on page 92

84. A column conundrum

Bob wrote down the numbers 1 to 9 on pieces of card and arranged them in two columns as below:

"I can make the two columns add up to the same total by moving just two cards," he announced to Sally. "Well, I can do it by moving only one, replied Sally.

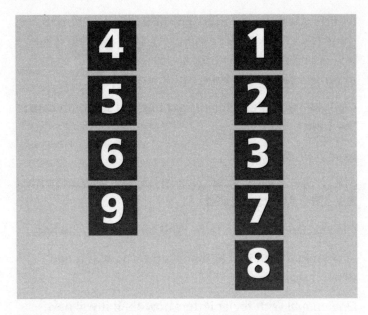

"Are you allowed to remove any of the numbers?" asked Fergus. "Of course not," they replied.

What were Bob and Sally's clever solutions?

Solution on page 97

....

85. Handshakes

"My people are not being polite enough," declared King Ogbad the Genteel to his courtiers. "By royal decree, all people must now shake hands more often. To make sure that this is carried out, I order you to count how many times each person shakes hands with another in the next year. And should your answers be even the slightest bit wrong, off with your heads!" he bellowed.

And so that year the courtiers journeyed throughout the land. Determined to record every handshake, they worked diligently throughout the day and often late into the night. At the end of the year the chief courtier was summoned by the king to announce the results.

"Sire, every greeting has been witnessed, every secret liaison has been spied, and every handshake has been recorded." Pointing to the vast stacks of paper piled to the palace ceiling he announced: "Here are the results which have taken several weeks to count. And the grand total was..."

"Silence!" ordered the King. "Tell me first, how many people shook hands an odd number of times?"

"Well, let me see ... it was 2143", replied the courtier after he had looked through his summary.

"Then you have miscounted!" roared King Ogbad. "Off with your heads the lot of you!"

How could the king (and you, for that matter) be so absolutely certain that the counting was wrong?

Solution on page 102

. . . .

86. Howzat?!

Roger turned up to watch his dad playing cricket, but since watching Geoffrey batting is far from interesting, he decided to do a circuit of the field on his

bicycle, going anticlockwise as indicated by the arrow.

After five minutes he arrived back at his starting point. Interestingly, in his whole journey he never once turned left. How did he do it?

Solution on page 107

....

87. Whodunnit?

Shortly before the trial of Charlie Snod, the police received a mysterious note from the infamous villain Henry van Eyck. It read as follows:

> *Regarding the current case concerning Charlie Snod, here are six statements on the matter:*
>
> 1. *The truth is that this statement and the one after the first true statement are not both true.*
>
> 2. *If you add the number of the first false statement to the number of the second true statement you get the number of a statement which is as true as number one.*
>
> 3. *Statement number two is a downright lie, I'm afraid.*
>
> 4. *Charlie Snod is innocent or I'm a Dutchman (or both).*
>
> 5. *At least half of these six statements are true.*

6. My own gang was responsible
   for the crime.

   Yours honestly

   Henry van Eyck.

Amazingly what he said turned out to be right. Who dunnit?

Solution on page 113

··

88. Coin circular

Annika puts a one glot coin and a five glot coin (which is twice the diameter of the one glot coin) on the table, as in the diagram. Both coins have a milled edge, and she now rolls the five glot coin around the edge of the one glot coin without it slipping till it gets back to where it started. She notices it is  upside down. She repeats, and finds the five glot coin is the right way up again.

How many complete revolutions has the five glot coin now been through?

Solution on page 117

89. Quirky Qwerty

When the typewriter was invented, there was a problem with the keys jamming with each other. To reduce the chance of this, the proprietor of the first patent mixed up the keyboard letters to slow down the typist. This is why the top row has the letters QWERTYUIOP. Now that we have computers, it would make sense to have more sensible lettering, but the world has invested so much money in QWERTYUIOP that it looks as though we are doomed to using it in perpetuity. But still, it does mean that a classic old puzzle still holds true.

Can you find a ten-letter word that uses letters only from the top row of the standard typewriter keyboard (but not necessarily all of them)? Indeed, can you find three such words?

Solution on page 124

90. The missing marbles

Uncle Herbert had a mean streak, and often liked to play tricks. When his four grandchildren found a small hoard of marbles in his loft, he told them that if they took a carrier bag each and put as many marbles as possible into each bag, they could take them home. They collected all the marbles they could find, which happened to be 40, and divided them fairly, ten each, in a carrier bag each.

Unfortunately Uncle Herbert wasn't satisfied, and the children took none of their new-found marbles home. What should they have done to satisfy Uncle Herbert?

Solution on page 128

64

91. Big crowd

The most interesting thing about last week's match between the bottom two teams in the Ruritanian Premier League was the size of the crowd, or so Max Splutzen, the club statistician, thought. He found that if he put a one in front of the crowd number and multiplied this new number by three, the result was the crowd number with one on the end. How big was the crowd?

1????? x 3 = ?????1

Solution on page 82

92. Bad line

The telephone rings in the office:

Caller: Can I talk to Mr Jardine, please.

Secretary: Who's speaking, please?

Caller: Paten.

Secretary: I'm sorry, it's a bad line.
Can you repeat that?

Caller: Paten. P for Pluto, A for Adolf, T for Tummy

Secretary: T for what sir ?

Caller: T for Tummy, E for Elephant, N for Nose.

According to an old puzzle, this conversation demonstrates that the secretary is not very intelligent. Why? And do you agree?

Solution on page 87

....
93. Doctored books

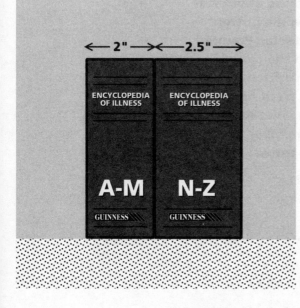

Dr Fitzgerald has an encyclopedia of illnesses which comes in two volumes: A-M and N-Z. The first volume is two inches thick and the second two and a quarter inches thick. Each cover is one eighth of an inch thick. At the end of a hard day's research, he puts a bookmark at Aaron's Syndrome, and another at Zyphoglactic Fever and returns the books correctly to the shelf.

How far apart are the two bookmarks?

Solution on page 92

....
94. A bun fight

Mrs Watson had just taken six hot and delicious buns from the oven for the children's tea – or so she thought. When she looked at them again, one of them had already gone. "You're the limit!" she cried to Emma and Pippa, "Now, you won't get any more. I shall eat them all myself."

Then she caught herself; she had no wish to put on more weight by eating five buns she didn't need.

"On second thoughts, you can do some extra homework. If you can work out how to divide the buns equally between you, without removing them from their tray, with one straight cut only, then you can have them for tea. Otherwise, Fido gets them."

Emma and Pippa were successful. In fact, they found diferent ways to divide the buns. How did they do it?

Solution on page 97

95. Beer mat bet

"I will bet you a fiver," said Gary to Marian, "that if we take turns to place beer mats on this table top, and I start, then you will be the first one who is not able to place a mat on the table! Of course," he added, "the mats must not overlap each other, or fall off the edge of the table."

The beer mats were all circular and identical in size, and the table top was a rectangle.

How did Gary plan to win this game?

Solution on page 102

96. The trick backfires

Unknown to Gary, Marian already knew the beer mat trick of puzzle 95. But despite this she agreed to the challenge. Gary did indeed place a mat in the middle of the table, and yet Marian ended up winning.

Can you explain how she did it?

Solution on page 108

97. Alf's cornet

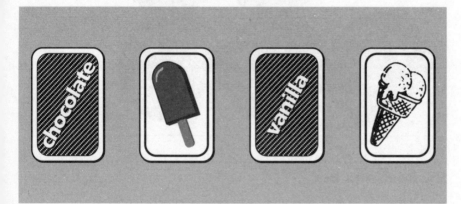

Here are four cards. All of the cards have a picture of an ice cream on one side and a flavour on the other side. "I think that every card with a lolly on one side has the word 'chocolate' on the other side," says Alf.

Which cards do you need to turn over to prove that Alf is right?

Solution on page 113

98. Add up trick

Charles decided to impress his father: "Write down any random seven-figure number please, then write down any other seven-figure number under the first one." His father did so.

"Now I will write one more number, and then I want you to write down another one, then I will write a second" said Charles. This was the result:

Dad's first number:	7,258,391
Dad's second number:	1,866,934
Charles's first number:	2,741,608
Dad's third number:	5,964,372
Charles's second number:	8,133,065

"Right," said Charles, "I bet I can add these numbers up in less than five seconds." "Nonsense, even with a calculator you couldn't do it that quickly," said his father. But in three seconds Charles had written down the answer to the sum, which was 25,964,370.

How did Charles do it?

Solution on page 118

99. The generation gap

"We now come," said the professor, scratching his nose, "to a most important historical figure, Ethelbert the Almost-Always Ready. He was almost certainly an ancestor of mine. Although I say so myself, I am also prepared for almost everything."

"Excuse me, Professor," interrupted his least favourite

student, "but you said earlier in your lecture that you were almost certainly descended from Matilda the Fascinating, and yesterday you claimed that Saint Peter Pauper's illegitimate son was your ancestor. How can you be so sure?"

The professor was, of course, ready for this objection. Why did the professor expect to be related to these assorted Saxons?

Solution on page 124

100. Shop reflection

Standing in the street in front of a shop window, I can see the name of the shop, in large gilt letters on the window itself, and I can also see it reflected in a mirror inside the shop.

Do I see the name on the mirror the right way round, or reversed?

Solution on page 128

101. Prize picking

On a rather unusual television game show called Bonanza, one of the contestants, Mavis, has a chance to win the star prize. "You have a choice of two unmarked envelopes," says the host, Jimmy. "One of them contains a certain sum of money which we will call 'X'. The other contains this week's Bonanza prize which is twice as much, or 'Double X'. It's up to you to choose the one with the most money." Mavis selects one of the envelopes.

"Now, you can still change your mind. You know that

there is a 50–50 chance that the other envelope contains the bonanza, with twice as much money, but equally it may have half as much money as the one you've picked. So since it is either double or half, then on average if you pick the other envelope it should have one-and-a-quarter times as much as the envelope you have got. So it looks like you should switch envelopes… but don't let me pressure you."

Should Mavis switch or stick with the one she has?

Solution on page 83

102. Catastrophe cat

Unfortunately for Sybil, the officers' cat, she has chosen to spend the night asleep on the top of the caterpillar track of one of the large tanks parked outside the camp. It is unfortunate because there is a military exercise at the crack of dawn, and the tank starts up and drives off at its regulation ten miles per hour.

The cat, clever enough to realize she might be on the verge of getting squashed but too sleepy to realize her best policy would be to jump off, instead starts running backwards along the caterpillar track.

How fast will Sybil have to run to avoid a grim fate?

Solution on page 87

103. Coloured hats

Professor Potts has set a tough challenge for his four brightest students, who are sat facing each other. He says "I have seven hats here, four black and three white. I will blindfold you and then give you each a hat. I will then remove the blindfolds and ask each of you in turn if you are able to work out what is the colour your hat." He does this. Each student thinks very hard before he speaks. And this is what each one says:

First student: I don't know.

Second student: I don't know, either.

Third student: Nor do I.

Before his blindfold is removed, the fourth student announces the colour of his hat. What is it, and how does he know?

Solution on page 93

104. Name prediction

Jane Higgins was walking down the high street when she bumped into an old friend. "Hello, I haven't seen or heard from you since graduation back in 1982!" said Jane, "what's happened to you?"

"Well, I got married in 1989 to somebody you wouldn't know. This is our son," said the friend, who was holding hands with a little boy.

"Hello, and what's your name?" said Jane to the boy.

"It's the same as Daddy's".

"Ah, so it's Peter is it?" said Jane.

How did Jane know?

Solution on page 98

105. Delete where appropriate

On January 2nd 1995 I said:

"My great aunt, who (was born/was married/died) on December 1st (1911/1913/1915), (is/was/would have been/will still be) (77,80,94) years old (last, next) (week, month, year)."

How many correct versions can you find from all the choices available?

Solution on page 102

106. Cheese, please

"Who wants cheese?" asked Mrs Smith. "We all do," said Peter, so Mrs Smith started to cut the cubical block into three equal slices in the obvious way. "Oh, no! Boring!" cried Gary, "we always have boring old blocks, we want something DIFFERENT." "Yes, let's have something new," said William, who didn't notice that

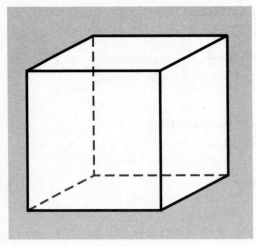

he was repeating what Gary had said.

Mrs Smith thought for a while, and then sliced the cube of cheese into three pieces, identical in shape, which used up the whole block, and looked nothing like the usual boring slices.

How did she do it?

(A word of advice – unless you have superhuman ability to see things in your head, it is helpful to cut cubes from cheese and experiment. Then you can eat the cheese later.)

Solution on page 108

....

107. Time travel

Some years ago the eccentric adventurer Bart Carruthers decided to fly his small plane single-handed around the world. He left London at noon on March 1st, and his route took him via Cairo, Hong Kong, Hawaii, New York and finally across the Atlantic. He arrived back in London only to discover there was no film in his camera, so he decided to do the whole trip again (following the same route). He arrived back in London at the end of his double marathon at noon on March 31st. Bart kept no diary, so to keep track of time he simply counted the total number of nights during his two journeys.

How many nights was that?

Solution on page 114

108. Telephone extension

Mike has thrown in his job at United Bottlewashers and from now on he is going to be working from home (as a bottlewashing consultant, naturally). His first step is to convert his back room into an office. As you can see, the room is 13 feet square and its ceiling is only 7 feet high. Mike has put a telephone socket in the middle of the back wall one foot up from the floor, and now he is bringing an extension cable from his main phone. But he has a problem. The extension cable coming in at the top corner above the door is only 20 feet long, and to be safe it must, at all points, be attached to the ceiling or wall or run under the carpet.

Can you find a way for the cable to reach the socket?

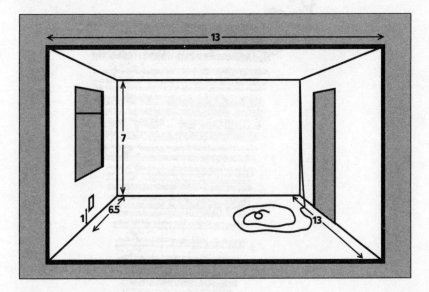

Solution on page 119

109. Guinness Mindbender

You've made it through the rest of the puzzles, so you deserve a drink. You might like to try a new cocktail, which appropriately enough is called a Guinness Mindbender. What you need is some Guinness, fresh cream, treacle, Irish whiskey... well, you get the picture. The thing is, this drink has a strange effect on some people – it makes them start thinking about a big number. In fact it is a huge number, in the billions.

You may not have the desire to drink it, but any ideas about the number?

Solution on page 128

The Solutions

1. The alternative nine dot puzzle
(puzzle, page 10)

Move the four corner coins as follows:

11. Turn four into five *(puzzle page 15)*

FOUR into FIVE: it can be done in seven steps, for example:

FOUR POUR POUT PORT PORE FORE FIRE FIVE

*ONE into TWO: using common words it can be done in
ten steps:*

ONE ODE ODD ADD AID LID LIP TIP TOP TOO TWO

*SEVEN into EIGHT: it is easier to solve this by working
backwards from EIGHT, since this is the trickier end. Although
lots of common words like MIGHT and FIGHT could come next,
they don't seem to lead anywhere. The word that does is
BIGHT. Here is our solution, in 13 steps:*

*EIGHT BIGHT BIGOT BEGOT BEGET BESET RESET REVET RIVET
RIVER RAVER SAVER SEVER SEVEN*

21. A knotty poser *(puzzle, page 21)*

In most places on the square piece
of wood where the knot might be
located, John could cut four
horizontal or four vertical pieces
that were at least 40 cm. A good
answer is to say that the knot
overlapped any of the intersections
of the lines shown in the diagram,
because if it did so, the four pieces
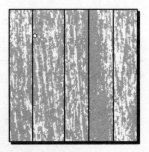
would have to be slightly less than 40 cm wide (with the
remaining wasted piece being slightly wider).

*In fact, the worst positions of all are A and B. If the knot was
in either of these positions then the planks could only be
39.2 cm wide at most, and 43.2 cm would be wasted.*

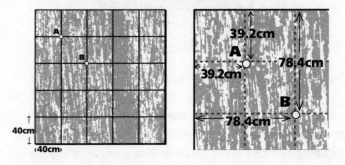

31. Interesting words *(puzzle, page 27)*

The three words are:

'FACETIOUS' – contains each of the vowels A,E,I,O,U in order.

*'STRENGTHS' – contains eight consonants (five consecutive)
and only one vowel, the highest ratio in a common word.*

'QUEUEING' – contains five consecutive vowels, the longest

sequence in a common word. (It can also be spelt QUEUING, which is much more dull.)

The unusual combinations of letters means that these are good words to use in the popular word game 'Hangman'.

41. Safe cracking *(puzzle, page 32)*

The code of the safe is 7095416238. The most useful clue is that the digits 0 to 9 are all used along the top and side of the grid. 0 times anything is 0, so the second column must be 0. One times anything can only have one digit, so the only possible place for 1 is the first row. Two times anything is even and is less than 20, so the only place left for 2 is the third row. And, since three times something is less than 30, the fourth row is the only place left for 3. Five must head the fourth column since one of the numbers ends in 5. And similar logic leads to all of the other digits.

51. Scattered vegetables *(puzzle, page 40)*

Potatoes is the most appropiate word. This has nothing to do with vegetables, though there may be some attempts at exotic *explanations concerning how easy it is to 'scatter' different vegetables. The explanation is very simple. The words in the sentence have increasing numbers of letters – one, two, three, four etc. The gap needs to be filled by a word containing eight letters, and so, of the five words supplied, only potatoes fits.*

61. Baywatch *(puzzle, page 46)*

Route B is slightly faster, which goes to show that the fastest route between two points is not always a straight line.

You can measure the lengths of routes A and B by using the following calculation:

Route A = $\sqrt{60 + 80}$ = 100 metres, of which 50 metres are in sand and 50 metres are in water.
Route A takes $^{50}/_2$ + $^{50}/_6$ = 33.33 seconds.

Route B = $\sqrt{30 + 80}$ = 85.4 metres in sand and 30 metres in water. Route B takes $^{85.4}/_6$ + $^{30}/_2$ = 29.2 seconds.

It is possible to go even faster than Route B. If Wayne aims straight for any point just short of the 80 metres and swims from there, his time goes down slightly. In fact if he aims for a point about 70 metres along the beach he can make it in 28.5 seconds. Let's hope Wayne's mental agility is up to his physique.

Incidentally, Wayne's fastest route is know as 'the path of shortest time'. The famous physicist Richard Feynman pointed out that when a beam of light passes through glass and refracts, it amazingly 'knows' which is the path of shortest time and it always takes that route.

71. Pointed stars *(puzzle, page 52)*

It can be done, but only with either a very imperfect hexagon or a very imperfect star. Notice it uses seven lines (drawn

A–B–C–D–E–F–G–A), but it is only six-pointed because the seventh 'point' (G) is inside the star.

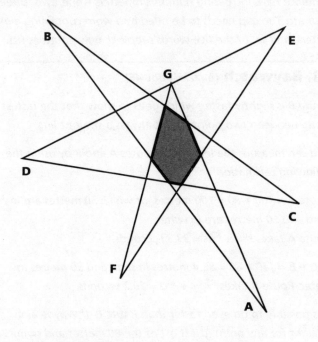

---

81. The glass that cheers *(puzzle, page 58)*

They could get their punch in five moves, by inverting (for example) 1–2–3, 4–5–6, 7–8–9, 8–9–10 and finally 8–9–11. Glasses 8 and 9, having each been inverted three times, are finally the correct way up, like the rest.

Of course, these are not the only combinations you could use to turn all the glasses in five moves but all involve the same principle.

---

91. Big crowd *(puzzle, page 65)*

The crowd was 42,857. (142,857 x 3 = 428,571). It may seem surprising that such a precise but dull-looking number could

be the only answer with so little information in the puzzle.

If you want to find this number, it helps to replace the numbers with letters.

Let's call the crowd size ABC..XYZ. Then we know that 1ABC..XYZ x 3 = ABC..XYZ1. Now if three times something ends in one, then that something can only end in 7 - so Z is 7 and 1ABC..XY7 x 3 = ABC..XY71. So 3 x Y + 2 (carried) ends in seven, which means Y can only be five. 3 x X + 1 (carried) ends in five, so X must be eight. Continuing this we finally get (1)42857, which multiplied by three = 42857(1). If this is not the answer, the next number which fits is 142857142857. This would mean a crowd of over 42 billion at the match – a little unlikely, you will agree.

The number 142857 has many interesting properties – see what happens when you multiply it by any number between two and seven, or when you add its first half to its second half.

101. Prize picking *(puzzle, page 70)*

It makes no difference at all if Mavis switches or sticks. The game show host is in fact endorsing a common fallacy by saying the average of the other envelope is one and a quarter times the one Mavis is holding. Suppose one envelope contains £500 and the other has the bonanza of £1000. She has an equal chance of winning either prize. If she has the £500 envelope and swaps, she will gain an extra £500. If she has the £1000 envelope and swaps, she will lose £500. So she has a 50–50 chance of gaining or losing £500, and if she was to play this game hundreds of times, then whatever her strategy she would still end up with an average of £750 per game. (If she had been allowed to open the envelope and found it had £500, so she knew that the other contained £250 or £1000, the question of whether she should swap or not becomes much trickier.)

2. Cricket for Americans *(puzzle, page 10)*

Diane could be confident that Brian, like most people quoting statistics, presented the figures in the way that made them sound most impressive.

Let us suppose Yorkshire did not win in 1931. That would mean that Brian would have been able to make the more impressive claim that Yorkshire had won seven times in the eight years up to 1939. And if Yorkshire had won in 1930, Brian would have said they won eight times in the ten years up to 1939, which again is more impressive. (In the same way, if a politician says unemployment has fallen for the last five months you can guarantee that six months ago it went up!)

12. Can you do it? *(puzzle, page 16)*

Fill the can to over half full, and tip it so that the water runs out until it reaches just from the lip of the can to the edge of the base, as in the first figure.

Now the can is one half full. Tilt the can upright and mark it inside to show how far up the water comes. Finally, tip out water a bit at a time, until when tilted, the water goes from the mark you scratched to the edge of the bottom, as in the second figure.

22. Elementary? *(puzzle, page 21)*

Watson was wearing a white handkerchief. If he had been wearing the blue handkerchief, Mrs Hudson would immediately have known that hers was one of the two white handkerchiefs. The fact that she didn't know means that she saw a white one on Watson's head.

This type of puzzle illustrates the interesting principle that sometimes you can make useful deductions from apparently 'no' information. There is a famous example from a real Sherlock Holmes story called Silver Blaze. *Inspector Gregory asks whether there is anything which Holmes wishes to draw to his attention:*

"To the curious incident of the dog in the night time" [replied Holmes].

"But the dog did nothing in the night time."

"That was the curious incident," remarked Sherlock Holmes.

32. Dawdling home *(puzzle, page 27)*

They are both right, because they are talking at cross-purposes. James says that if they have no idea when the bus is expected anyway, it doesn't matter when they turn up at the bus stop. This is true – if you dash to the bus stop, you may sometimes be lucky and catch a bus you would otherwise have missed, in which case you save a lot of time waiting. But very often you will not catch a bus you would have missed, and will simply have to wait that much longer for the bus you do catch. On balance, the two possibilities cancel each other out, and your average expected waiting time is the same whenever you turn up. (Of course, if you know something about the bus timetables the situation is entirely different.)

Jane is talking only of getting home as soon as possible, quite a different matter, and of course she wants to hurry, to catch the first available bus – even at the risk of waiting longer if one doesn't come soon.

42. Pencils ready! *(puzzle, page 34)*

There are many ways to do this: here are three possible methods. If, in your solution, you count not only the number of lines removed but also their total length, then the third diagram shows the 'shortest' answer.

52. The vanishing square *(puzzle, page 40)*

This is a trick. The extra square is in fact 'created' because there is a very thin gap along the diagonal. The diagram shows how the re-made rectangle would appear.

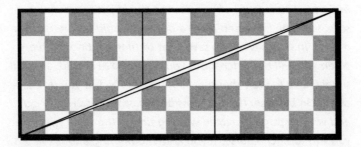

The gap is neither black nor white, of course, and the 'square' in the middle is half black and half white.

62. Pyramid puzzle *(puzzle, page 47)*

The angle was still 60 degrees. Angles don't change when they are magnified.

72. T-shirt teaser *(puzzle, page 53)*

The label is now on the outside of his left sleeve.

82. Pardon me, boys *(puzzle, page 58)*

Yes. The fastest time in which they can shine the shoes is seven minutes. Mike puts polish on the shoes of two of the men while Merv puts it on the third man's shoes. Merv then shines the shoes of Mike's two customers while Mike shines Merv's one.

Mike: Polish Mr A	*Polish Mr B*	*Shine Mr C*
Merv: Polish Mr C	*Shine Mr A*	*Shine Mr B*

92. Bad line *(puzzle, page 65)*

The traditional answer to this is that, since the secretary has established that the third letter is T, there is no need for her to know what it stands for.

However, it is clear from their conversation that they have a bad telephone line. T for Tummy sounds very like D for Dummy, so it is natural for her to ask for the caller to repeat the T (although a better response would have been "Sorry, is that T for Tango?").

102. Catastrophe cat *(puzzle, page 71)*

Sybil must run at 20 miles per hour just to stay still. The caterpillar track in contact with the ground is stationary, and the track at the top of the wheels therefore goes twice as fast as the tank itself.

3. Fun run go slow *(puzzle, page 11)*

It does not matter how fast she runs – even a world record sprint could not increase her average speed to six miles per hour. This is because the Fun Run is three miles long, so if her overall speed was six miles per hour she would do the whole run in 30 minutes. But she has already taken 30 minutes to run the first two miles at four miles per hour, so she would have to run the final mile in zero minutes! (This is a good illustration of the fact that averages can be quite complicated. You usually can't average an average.)

13. Less or fewer *(puzzle, page 16)*

*It would not be right to say either: there are in fact exactly six f's in the sentence. ('The **F**ighting **F**orces that are sa**F**ely stationed south o**F** the border are short o**F** motor **F**uel.') Many people only see four or five of the f's.*

*To answer the grammatical part of the question, there are **fewer** than seven f's. Strictly speaking, 'fewer' should be used when you are talking about things that can be counted (such as tins of soup, letters or people). 'Less' should be used when you are talking about a part of a single 'uncountable' thing (such as time or cheese or soup).*

23. Shorter circuit *(puzzle, page 22)*

Grommet's anticlockwise trip was shorter because when driving anticlockwise he is, of course, on the inner circle. He will save less than 100 metres.

To find the circumference of a circle you multiply the radius by 2π. Grommet's anticlockwise motorway radius was about six lanes smaller than his clockwise circle, and a motorway lane is just under three metres wide. So the anticlockwise circumference was smaller by 2 x π x 6 x 3 which is roughly 100 metres.

The next time you want to do a circuit of the M25, you could shorten your journey by up to 100 metres by travelling anticlockwise.

33. Screw on your thinking cap! *(puzzle, page 28)*

They do not move closer together or further apart.

To see why, imagine that there is a block of wood between them. The right-hand screw is being screwed as if it were screwing into the block, so the wooden block is being pulled towards the right.

The left-hand screw, however, is being turned as if it was

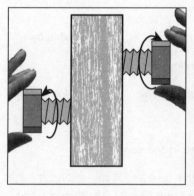

being unscrewed from the same wooden block. In other words, it is releasing it to allow it to move to the right. So the two bolts do not move relative to each other (apart from their separate rotations), and only the imaginary block moves. Take away the imaginary block...

43. Faulty scoring *(puzzle, page 34)*

In tennis, the difference between 30-all and deuce is purely psychological: the two scores are exactly equivalent, since to win a game in either situation one player needs to win two points in a row. Whenever a game reaches 30-all the umpire could therefore always call deuce.

Love-all, however, is not the same as 30-all. In all serious tennis matches the server is more likely to win a point than the receiver, but it takes a bit of maths (or a lot of experience of playing tennis) to prove that it is more of an advantage to the server (Tuttle) if the score is love-all than if it is 30-all. (In fact, if the server's chance of winning any point is always 60%, then his chance of winning the game from love-all is about 74%, while his chance of winning from 30-all is only 69%.)

53. Fair shares for all *(puzzle, page 41)*

There were 19 boys in the gang.

The puzzle includes three different whole numbers of sweets for sharing, depending on how many members of the gang are present. We don't know what these numbers are but we know that these numbers can be equally divided amongst different numbers of the boys:

	Divisible by:
Starting number of sweets minus two	*5*
Starting number of sweets minus one	*4 and 7*
Starting number of sweets	*3 and 'G'*

(G = the number of members in the gang.)

The middle number is divisible by 4 and 7, suggesting it might be 28? No, because the set of numbers 27, 28, 29 doesn't fit. What about 56? Yes that fits, because 55 is divisible by 5 and 57 by 3 – which means the number in the gang is 19. The next lowest set that fit is 475, 476 and 477 which would mean 159 in the gang – and that would rather stretch belief.

63. Football table *(puzzle, page 48)*

Dippleton v Bimpley has not been played – in fact, it is the only game left to be played in the league.

The number of matches played in this type of football league is always exactly half the number of points (because each game produces two points). That means that so far there have been five games out of the total of six. The other vital clue is goal difference – if you beat a team, your goal difference increases by at least one. This means Dippleton have only played two matches (0–0 and 1–1 or 1–0 and 0–1), and Chinfield must have played all three of their games to get four points with a goal difference of only one – win–win–loss, or win–draw–draw.

*Suppose D(ippleton) **have** played B(impley). B has not scored any goals yet and D has only scored one, so either it was 0–0, or else 1–0 to D.*

If D versus B was 0–0, then D's other point must have come from a 1–1 draw, which would have to be its only other match, so it was against Chinfield. But then who did Argleford score their three goals against? It isn't possible! And if D v B was 1–0, B must have played two more games (0–0 and 0–1) which again makes it impossible for Argleford to have scored three goals in two games.

In fact, similar logic will enable you to discover the results of all the matches already played:
A v B 2–0 ; A v C 1–1 ; A v D 0–1 ; C v D 1–0; and C v B 0–0.

73. Secret number club *(puzzle, page 53)*

The writer of the message has the special number '4'. He has of course added this number to each of the numbers in the message since that is the rule of the club, so there are six members in the club, all with numbers between 2 and 5, two of whom have a smaller number than him, and all of the numbers add up to 23. (One possible combination would be 2, 3, 4, 4, 5, 5.) If his number was bigger than 4, it would fall outside the range of numbers that he says members have; if his number was smaller than 4, then it would be impossible for there to be other members with smaller numbers than his.

83. Old MacDonald *(puzzle, page 59)*

Old MacDonald's collection of animals was:

PIG (piglet)

KID (goat)

OX (oxen)

SHEEP (sheep)

Some might say that it is slightly unusual to have an ox on the same farm as a pig, a sheep and a kid, but that's the way it was. If you said deer instead of sheep, that would be right as well.

93. Doctored books *(puzzle, page 66)*

The thickness of the two covers of the book – a quarter of an inch. The first page in the A-M book is on the right when the books are on the shelf, and the last page of N-Z is on the left. Most people think it is the exact opposite and say four inches.

ENCYCLOPEDIA
OF ILLNESS

ENCYCLOPEDIA
OF ILLNESS

A-M N-Z

GUINNESS

GUINNESS

103. Coloured hats *(puzzle, page 72)*

He says: "I am wearing a black hat."

This uses similar principles to puzzle 22.

The fourth student reasons as follows: "Suppose my hat is white. The first three students have already tried to work out the colour of their hats and failed. If number two could see white hats on number three and me, then he could deduce his hat must be black (because if it was white, number one would have known his was black). But number two said nothing, so if mine was white number three would know that his hat was black. But since number three also said nothing, the only explanation is that I must be wearing a black hat."

4. Pam's party *(puzzle, page 11)*

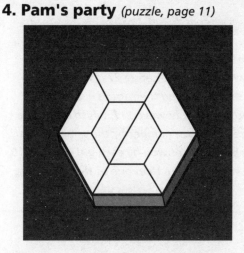

This is the simplest and prettiest solution.

14. Fair prizes *(puzzle, page 17)*

She won five prizes.

There were only four girls involved, and six differences

between them were given. Therefore every possible difference between the four girls was named and we are looking for four numbers whose six differences are 1, 2, 3, 4, 5 and 6. The differences between numbers don't change if all the numbers are increased or decreased by the same amount, so we can start by assuming that the first number is one, in which case the largest number (to give a maximum difference of six), must be seven.

$$1 \_\_ \_\_ 7$$

We have to fill in the two middle numbers so that the six differences are the numbers 1 to 6. There are just two ways to do this:

1 2 5 7 or 1 3 6 7

The total number of prizes won in the first case is 1 +2 + 5 + 7 = 15, which can be raised to 27 if we add three prizes to each girl's total, making their totals 4, 5, 8 and 10. The total of the second set is, however, 17, which cannot be raised to 27 by increasing each number by the same amount. Therefore the number of prizes won by each girl is 4, 5, 8, 10, and Bernice, who won one more than one of the other girls, won five prizes.

24. An Olympic effort *(puzzle, page 23)*

This is one possible route:

Although Daniel had to visit all the corners twice, he was able to turn sharply to avoid going over his previous tracks.

34. True or false *(puzzle, page 28)*

Since all of the statements contradict each other, three of them must be false. Therefore statement number three is true and the others are false.

44. A six pack *(puzzle, page 35)*

Unlike magic squares made of numbers, in which the diagonals are expected to have the same property as the rows and columns, the diagonals of word squares are usually meaningless.

In this case, that is not so, and the words fit into the rows and columns and both diagonals.

54. A jugful of trouble *(puzzle, page 42)*

As the puzzle makes plain, the two containers are simply cylinders, so you can half-fill either one exactly by filling it so that the water just reaches the bottom edge and the top edge

of the can, as in our sketch. (See also puzzle 12.)

So you can fill the containers twice each from the tap, to transfer a total of 11 + 7 + 5.5 + 3.5 = 27 pints.

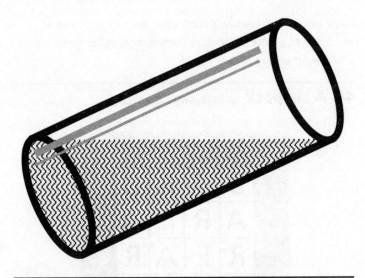

64. T for two *(puzzle, page 48)*

First man: Twenty-one.

Second man: Twenty-two.

There are nineteen 't's in the puzzle, but nineteen and twenty are not correct answers because their 't's have to be included in the answer. There are other possible correct answers that are slightly more contrived. For example, 'twenty-three times' and 'twenty-four times in total', or 'dix-neuf', and 'vingt' if the two men were French.

74. Mirror writing *(puzzle, page 54)*

The word that becomes decoded is 'DECODED'. It is unchanged when you look at it upside down in the mirror (have a look and see). The reason is that all the letters in that

word are symmetrical both at the top and the bottom. All the
other words contain at least one letter which does not have
this line of symmetry.

84. A column conundrum *(puzzle, page 59)*

Bob moved the one and three, Sally inverted the nine.

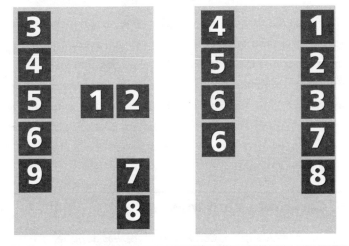

94. A bun fight *(puzzle, page 66)*

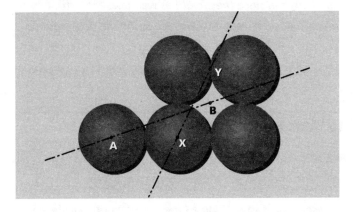

Any line through X will divide the bottom row of three buns
fairly, and any line through Y will divide the top two fairly, so

the line XY is one solution to their problem. Similarly, any line through A bisects the left-hand bun and any line through B (the midpoint of the group) bisects the block of four buns on the right, so the other solution is the line AB.

104. Name prediction *(puzzle, page 72)*

The friend is a man called Peter. For some reason most people assume that Jane's friend must be a woman, even though there is nothing to indicate this in the puzzle, and even though it is common for college friends to be of the opposite sex. Interestingly, people have the same difficulty when all the sexes in the puzzle are reversed. (This is a variant of the more famous 'surgeon' puzzle which appeared in The Guinness Book of Brainteasers.*)*

5. Christmas card mystery *(puzzle, page 12)*

The most likely explanation is that there was a special deal: buy ten cards and get one (or two) free. This means nobody would buy ten since they might as well take the extra two for the same price. In fact, this is a true story: the deal was 50p per card or 12 for £5. So, while buying 5, 15 or 20 cards was cheaper than buying 6, 16 or 21, buying ten was no cheaper than buying 11.

15. Mrs Bearskin's quilt *(puzzle, page 17)*

Five pieces are indeed not necessary. She could manage with only four, and also get the pretty pattern on the left.

Or, if she wants something a little less symmetrical, she could move the cuts sideways and get a pattern like the one on the right.

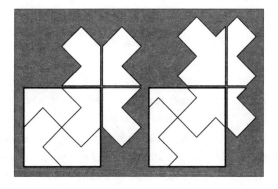

25. Inverted clock *(puzzle, page 23)*

Yes – the little hand would always be slightly out of position. For example, if Tom tried to set the clock at noon, the big hand would be at 12 but the little hand would be half way between 11 and 12 or between 12 and 1, because the real time would be half past five or half past six. (Interestingly, this shows that if the numbers on a clock were replaced by marks, you could always tell which was its right way up.)

35. Spotting doobreys *(puzzle, page 29)*

The reason is simple: the birds spend much longer away from the nest (over 15 minutes) than they do in the nest within sight of Edward Spinks (under 30 seconds), so the chance is more than 29:1 that the first sighting will be a bird flying back to the nest. Since he has only been watching for a week, it is no surprise that so far Mr Spinks's first sightings have always been arrivals. (If Mr Spinks started watching before dawn, of course, his first sighting would be of a bird leaving the nest.)

45. Christmas birthdays *(puzzle, page 36)*

It is January 1st. In any year, Christmas Day is 358 (or 359) days later than New Year's Day, so the day of the week is always different. Damien's birthday is on 31st December, which explains how his birthday can appear to leap by so much. And Janet (who may not be present at this gathering) lives somewhere in the southern hemisphere.

55. A weighty problem *(puzzle, page 43)*

He picked six parcels and weighed three against three.

If one side of the balance was lighter than the other, he would know that the light parcel was one of those three. He would then compare the weights of two of the three parcels on the light side. The light parcel would be either the lighter of the two, or else the one he didn't weigh if the other two balanced.

If the three against three at the start balanced, then the light parcel would be one of the other three and he would weigh one against one in the same way as before.

65. A dicey cube *(puzzle, page 49)*

The number opposite four is six. Most people say three, but

this is not an ordinary die because it has two sixes and no five. To see why, look at the two and six in the first two diagrams. In one, the two slopes to the left, in the other it slopes to the right, so there must be different faces involved. If it is the same six in both views then three and four end up on the same face, so the two sixes must be different. Here is what the whole cube looks like unfolded:

75. He who hesitates is lost *(puzzle, page 54)*

Mr Pendlebury was 200 metres short of the second bus stop.

It helps to draw the positions:

A	B	<-100 metres->	C	D
STOP 2	Mr P		STOP 1	BUS

If Mr P sprints to STOP 1, he will meet the bus there. But the bus moves at three times his speed, so the distance DC = 3 x CB = 300. If he sprints to STOP 2 he meets the bus there, so DA = 3 x BA.

So DA = 3 x BA = BA + 400; so 2 x BA = 400, and thus BA = 200 metres.

So Mr P was twice as far from the second stop as he was from the first. There was no need for the puzzle to mention 100 metres – this ratio of 2:1 from the two stops would be true whatever the distance walked.

85. Handshakes *(puzzle, page 60)*

Whenever you shake hands with somebody the total number of handshakes that have been made is two (because the other person shook hands with you at the same time). So the total number of handshakes in the country must have been even.

This means that the number of people who shook hands an odd number of times must also have been even, which according to the courtier was not the case. Hence he lost his head.

95. Beer mat bet *(puzzle, page 67)*

Gary had heard this trick before and knew that the secret was to put a mat exactly in the middle of the table. Then wherever Marian put a mat, he would put one symmetrically opposite, so that when it became impossible to place a mat it would be Marian who reached this situation first.

105. Delete where appropriate *(puzzle, page 73)*

My great aunt, who was born on December 1st 1915, will still be 80 years old next year.

My great aunt, who was born on December 1st 1913, was 80 years old last year (until December 1st).

And you can replace the will be/was with 'would have been' in both of the above if she died before 1994.

6. Typewriter trouble *(puzzle, page 13)*

Sue sent the letter. Every time the letter 'z' is printed, the daisywheel shifts round by one (except for full stops, which still print correctly). Z appears six times in the message, so the wheel shifts round six times in total. The rest of the message reads:

Every time I type the letter z it starts to go funny. I must get it fixed when I come home. Lots of love. Sue.

16. A borderline case *(puzzle, page 18)*

In a way they are all right! Rivers make up part of the Spain-Portugal border. A mathematician called Hugo Steinhaus pointed out that the length of a river depends on the size of the ruler that you use to measure it. In particular, he said that if you use a small ruler and trace its banks in and out of every little creek and inlet, every twist and turn in the bank, then you will end up with a total length far in excess of the length calculated from a map, or given in geography books.

So when the Spanish claimed years ago that their boundary with Portugal was 987 km long, they were probably correct, by the scale they used to measure it, and the Portuguese may well have been correct when they claimed that it was 1214 km long. Pamela is most likely to be wrong, because if she really tried to get down on her hands and knees and measured the length of the border with a school ruler she would end up with a total length far more than 2000 km.

26. Do you get the picture? *(puzzle, page 24)*

You can see how it is possible with some figures. For the sake of simplicity, let's suppose that each collector has just two pictures:

	Nigel	Fred	Percy
value of the pictures (£m)	8, 7	6, 6	7, 4
after first transaction	8	7, 6, 6	7, 4
after second transaction	8	7, 6	7, 6, 4

In the first transaction, Nigel gets rid of his cheapest picture which becomes Fred's most expensive, so both averages rise. In the second, Fred sells to Percy a picture whose value is less than the average of his three pictures, but higher in value than Percy's average. So everyone's average has gone up.

This phenomenon explains how it would be possible, for example, for one person to move from one county to another and in doing so raise the average IQ of both counties. Indeed, it would be possible to raise the average IQ of every county in the UK in this way.

36. Mustafa square *(puzzle, page 30)*

The number is 9376. Although there are some elegant ways of finding this number using some neat algebra, you can actually find it with a calculator by trial and error very quickly – as long as you realize that the last three digits must be the same as one of Mustafa's three-digit solutions (376 and 625). Taking 376 first, you try 1376, 2376, 3376 and so on until you get to 9376, which when squared is 87909376.

So why is there no second number? Well, using Mustafa's other three digit solution, 625, you can try 1625, 2625, 3625 and so on, but none of these work - unless you also try 0625, which when squared does indeed end 0625! But 0625 is really the same as 625. So, strictly speaking, 9376 is the only four-digit number that works.

Solutions with the same number of digits form a pattern when you add them:

5 + 6 = 11

25 + 76 = 101

625 + 376 = 1001

0625 + 9376 = 10001

And so on. The pattern only works if you count 0625 as a four-digit number, which Mustafa did not.

46. Ring in the ring road *(puzzle, page 37)*

The total length of West Street and Chuch Street is neither greater nor less than the total length of Walden Road and The Circus: the pairs of roads are of equal total length. There is a neat way of illustrating this. Imagine that one of the straight main roads is moved, parallel to itself, as in the diagram.

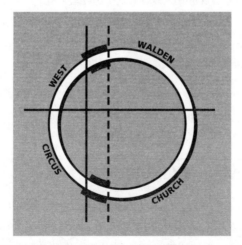

The length of West Street has increased by the curved portion in heavy line at the top, but its partner, Church Street, has decreased in length by exactly the same amount, as shown by the heavy line at the bottom. On balance, therefore, their

total length has not changed at all. The same is true, for the same reason, of the total length of Walden Road and The Circus.

Moving the horizontal road parallel to itself would also not alter the lengths of the pairs of the roads. The total lengths of each pair would remain the same. So, in order to compare the actual total lengths of each pair, we can move both roads until they pass through the centre of the circle. It can then immediately be seen that the total lengths of each pair are equal to each other, and also equal to one half of the circumference of the whole ring road.

56. Superball rebound *(puzzle, page 43)*

The somewhat surprising answer is that the ball rebounds at 120 mph. Its speed, relative to the train before impact, is 20 + 50 = 70 mph. It will therefore bounce back at 70 mph relative to the train. (This is the answer that many people give.) But the train is going at 50 mph, so the actual speed at which the ball rebounds towards Craig is 70 + 50 = 120 mph.

An advanced physicist might argue that strictly the answer of 120 mph is not exactly true unless the train is infinitely heavy. But for the rest of us it is the right answer.

66. Leave and let die *(puzzle, page 49)*

One thing James Bond will not die of is freezing. All that a freezer does is transfer heat from its inside to its outside, and it uses a lot of electricity to do so. Since the freezer's outside is in the room, the room will in fact slowly warm up.
So Bond is more at risk of dying of dehydration, suffocation or overheating!

76. Card money *(puzzle, page 55)*

One player wins £12, one wins £8, and one poor chap loses £30. Let's call the four players A, B, C and D, with A being the winner of the £10.

The only combination that wins £10 is if A wins the 900- and 1100-point games and loses the 1000-point game. Suppose A wins the 900-point game with B and the 1100-point game with C. Then he must lose the 1000-point game with D, so B and C were the winners of that game. The overall points are as follows:

	900	1100	1000
Winners:	*A & B*	*A & C*	*B & C*
Losers:	*C & D*	*B & D*	*A & D*

So A won £20 and lost £10, B won £19 and lost £11 (net win £8), C won £21 and lost £9 (net win £12), and poor old D lost £30 and won nothing.

86. Howzat?! *(puzzle, page 61)*

He turned right instead (naturally, what else could she do?) like this:

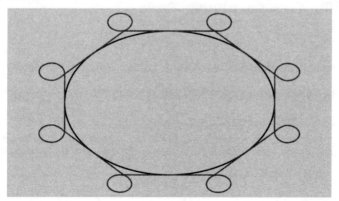

No one asked about how short his curious journey might have been, but the answer would look something like the above. He cycles along the sides of a polygon that can be drawn round the ground, and at each corner, he pirouettes to the right.

96. The trick backfires *(puzzle, page 68)*

In theory, of course, you can put a circular beer mat down in the exact centre of a rectangular table, or symmetrically opposite another one. In practice, however, it is almost impossible to do so exactly. When Gary placed the first mat, Marian placed her mat right next to it so that Gary could not precisely match it without overlapping his original mat. For several moves she continued to place her mats right next to each of Gary's, so his cunning strategy was defeated. The probability of Gary winning was therefore severely reduced and this allowed Marian, with a modicum of good luck, to triumph.

106. Cheese, please *(puzzle, page 73)*

This is how it is done. It is not easy to visualize, so we have shown the original cube on the left, and exploded it to show the three separate (identical) pieces around it.

This solution comes from the fact that when you look at a cube along any of its long diagonals, its outline is the shape of a hexagon. The three cuts are across the opposite sides of the hexagon.

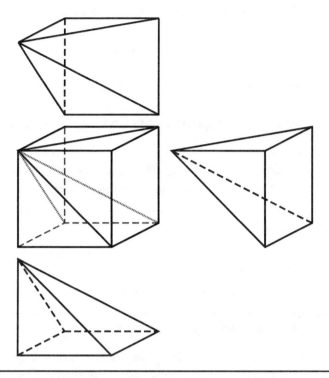

7. One 'ell of a puzzle *(puzzle, page 13)*

Any square at all can be left empty, by placing the five tiles suitably. The easiest way to see this is to first make this arrangement:

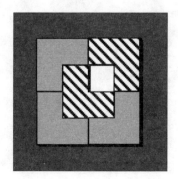

By rotating the central tile, any of the central squares can be left empty. However, by rotating the corner tile which surrounds two sides of whichever central square is left empty, you can leave any square in that quarter of the board empty. So all possible empty squares have been accounted for.

17. Not Mornington Crescent *(puzzle, page 18)*

South Ealing and Mansion House are the only two tube stations that contain all five vowels. Mansion House contains two o's, but South Ealing contains each vowel exactly once.

27. Fast food *(puzzle, page 25)*

It will take them three minutes. One pizza maker takes three minutes to cook one pizza, so in the same amount of time six pizza makers would make six pizzas.

37. Match this... *(puzzle, page 30)*

Rachel did it by using the fourth match to gently raise the two welded matches just enough to release the third match, which fell onto the fourth match. Then she carefully lifted the tripod, as shown in the diagram.

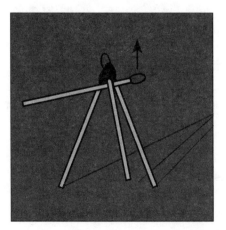

47. Test your mental vision *(puzzle, page 37)*

The answer is 'yes', after a total of 12 moves. This sort of sequence of moves was the basis of solutions to the famous 'Rubik's cube'.

The diagram on the left shows a view of the die at the start. After the four moves the die looks like the diagram on the right. The die has simply been rotated anticlockwise around the corner nearest to us – each face has moved around by one turn.

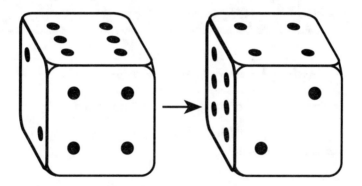

So in order to return the die to its original position you need to rotate it twice more by repeating the four moves twice. This makes 12 moves in total.

57. A noticeable problem *(puzzle, page 44)*

On second thoughts, Ravioli realized that he was much further away from the sign than the Inspector Grabber figure – the figure shows the actual situation – and so, although he could see most of the inspector, the inspector could see nothing of him as long as they both stood still.

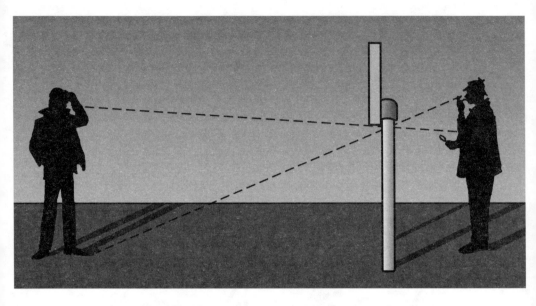

67. Midnight mayhem *(puzzle, page 50)*

The first movement of the girls is shown in the middle figure, and the next movement in the third figure. The top middle dorm is the empty one.

	8		6
10	5	2	3
	1		1
8	2	4	2

6	0	4
1		1
3	2	3

		10		8
8	5	0	3
	3		3
6	2	2	2

77. A classic stick trick *(puzzle, page 55)*

One. The top match is raised slightly, to reveal a small but perfect square in the middle.

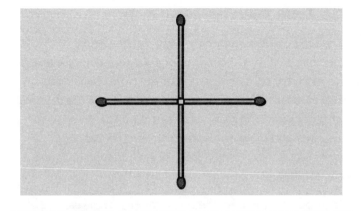

87. Whodunnit? *(puzzle, page 62)*

Charlie Snod did it.

*Suppose the first statement is false. That would mean that 'this statement and the one after the first true statement **are** both true' – which is a contradiction since we said the first was false. So the first statement must be true. This means statement two is false, which means statement three is true. So (from two being false), statement five is false. If five is false then less than half of the statements are true, and the only way for this to happen is if statements four and six are also false. So, from statement four, Charlie Snod must be guilty (and Henry van Eyck is not a Dutchman).*

97. Alf's cornet *(puzzle, page 68)*

You have to turn over two cards – the lolly card and the vanilla card. If the lolly card doesn't have chocolate on the other side, then Alf is wrong. And if the vanilla card has a lolly on the other side, then he is also wrong. But it doesn't matter what is on the other side of the other two cards: there could be any ice cream on the back of a chocolate card, since what Alf said did not exclude this possibility!

107. Time travel *(puzzle, page 74)*

Although he was actually only away for 30 days, he experienced 32 days and nights: one for each day, plus one for each eastward circumnavigation of the world. When you travel eastwards the sun goes overhead faster so the days and nights get shorter. In Jules Verne's Around The World in 80 Days, *the plot hinges on the fact the hero Phileas Fogg experiences 81 'days' on his journey even though he is only away for 80 days.*

On the other hand, since the circumference of the earth is about 24,000 miles, if you flew westwards around the equator at about 1000 mph your nights could last an eternity. Any faster and the sun would start setting in the east! (Incidentally, the International Date Line is irrelevant to this puzzle.)

8. Magic beans *(puzzle, page 14)*

Uncle Norman knew that whatever number of beans were picked up, the number would always finish up at 13 (eight in the right hand and five in the left).

For example, if you pick up 15 to start with:

	Left hand	Right hand	Total
Start	15	15	30
Four across	11	19	30
Return left to jar	0	19	19
Same no. from right hand	0	8	8
Pick up five	5	8	13

Bingo!

This is a quite straightforward little puzzle. Interestingly, it was invented by the great Leonardo da Vinci, who, as well as being a brilliant painter, inventor and engineer, was also keen

on mathematical tricks. Naturally, Leonardo's version did not refer to Uncle Norman.

18. Extended intervals *(puzzle, page 19)*

A simple delay this morning should mean that every train runs the same number of minutes late, in which case the intervals between trains will not be affected at all.

28. Lucky friends *(puzzle, page 25)*

They don't have lucky friends, since none of the people who won money were their friends! In fact, there is very little which is surprising about this story. Let's take David's sister, since she has the report of the biggest win. How many people could her story have come from? There are probably around 1000 children in her school, each of whom has perhaps ten adult relatives who would count as 'their family'. That makes 10,000 people and therefore 10,000 possible sources for the story. And, if in the last four weeks those 10,000 people bought 20,000 tickets between them (which is quite possible) then it becomes really quite likely that one family among them would achieve a £1000 win. Stories of big wins spread like wildfire, but nobody is interested in the 19,999 tickets that don't win. The same principle applies to the brother's and father's lottery stories.

38. A minor case *(puzzle, page 31)*

Watson realized that only children proceed right, right, left, left, right, right... and only when they are 'skipping' along, which also explains why the footprints are rather scuffed. So the culprit was a child, no doubt one of the family paying an illegal visit to the pantry.

48. Polar bearings *(puzzle, page 38)*

To your left. East is to the right when you travel north, but if you are travelling south (which you must be doing if you are leaving the North Pole) east is to the left.

58. The key question *(puzzle, page 45)*

The most keys Harold can hang without having a hook midway between them is four, as you will find if you try it. There is a very elegant way of proving this which involves giving the hooks co-ordinates similar to those on a map grid.

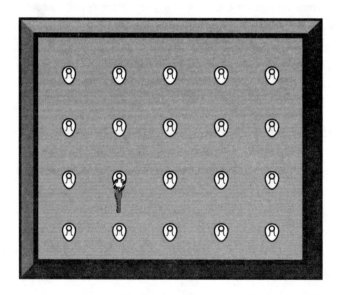

There is one key hanging in the diagram and it has co-ordinates 2,3 (2 across, 3 down). Since 2 is even and 3 is odd, we can say that this key's co-ordinates are even-odd. You will find that in order to be able to hang four keys that meet Harold's rule, their co-ordinates have to be even-odd, even-even, odd-even and odd-odd. For example, keys at 2,1; 2,4; 3,4 and 1,3 would work. But if Harold tries to hang a fifth key, its

position relative to one other key has to be even-even, which means there is certain to be a hook midway between it and one other key.

68. Twin tea bags *(puzzle, page 51)*

No, he is wrong. He is just as likely to pull out a single as a double. The reason for this is that to empty a jar of each of its 40 tea bags, Bill must first pull out the double tea bag (once) and then later pull out the remaining single tea bag (once) so he will pull out 20 doubles and 20 singles. If for any reason he is more likely to pull out doubles at the start of the jar, then this only means that at the end of the jar he is even more likely to pull out the singles that he has created. Since he can't remember how full the jar was, it turns out that the answer must be 50–50.

78. Surprise meal *(puzzle, page 56)*

Arguably, there was nothing wrong with her reasoning. This is a version of a well-known paradox called 'the unexpected hanging', which has been discussed endlessly by many authors. Here is one way in which you might explain the paradox: it is illogical to tell someone when they will have a surprise. The story could be cut down to Andrew saying: "Jenny, I'm going to give you a surprise this evening – I will take you for a meal at the Tandoori." She might logically say "That's not a surprise because you've told me," so that when he then actually does take her for the meal, she is slightly surprised.

88. Coin circular *(puzzle, page 63)*

The five glot coin has been through three revolutions. One of these is because it has travelled exactly the length of its circumference. The other two are because it has gone twice around the one glot coin. The diagram shows that the five

glot coin completes its first full revolution when it has gone
just two thirds of the way around the one glot coin. You can
help to prove this to yourself by using an old two pence piece
which is nearly twice the diameter of a new five pence piece.

98. Add up trick *(puzzle, page 69)*

Charles's numbers were not chosen at random. As he wrote
down his numbers, he made sure that each digit in his first
number when added to each digit of his father's first number
always added up to 9, and the same for the second numbers.
Charles's and Dad's first two numbers would then always be
equal to 9,999,999 + 9,999,999 = 19,999,998. Then, all he had
to do to add the five numbers was take his father's third
number, add 20,000,000 and take away 2 - a very simple
calculation, which can be done by putting a 2 in front of dad's
third number and subtracting 2 from its end.

Dad's first number	7 2 5 8 3 9 1
	+
Charles's first number	2 7 4 1 6 0 8
=	9 9 9 9 9 9 9

108. Telephone extension *(puzzle, page 75)*

The only way is for the cable to go diagonally across the wall and under the carpet, as shown in diagram B. It gets there with about six inches to spare. To find the shortest route, imagine the room as a box folded up from a flat piece of cardboard. If you unfold the room, there are two promising arrangements for getting from the top corner to the socket in a straight line (which is the shortest route). You can either measure or calculate the distances. In A this turns out to be 20.4 feet. In B it is actually 19.4 feet. (Approaches using the ceiling and other walls are all longer.)

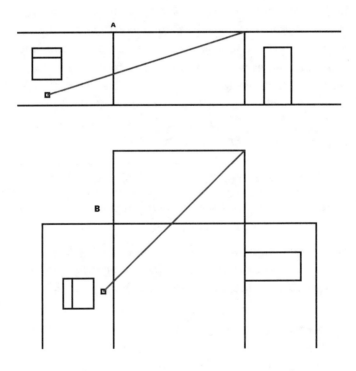

9. Missing the bus *(puzzle, page 15)*

The reason is that if he sees a bus leaving his stop, on average he has to wait a shorter time for the next one than if he doesn't see one leaving

To see why, imagine seeing a bus leave the stop. It could be the first, second or third in the bunch, so his wait will be either 30 seconds (after the first two) or 14 minutes – which averages a five-minutes wait. If he doesn't see a bus leave, then he has arrived in the long gap, so his wait is going to be between 0 and 14 minutes, or about seven minutes on average. So on average he waits two minutes more if he doesn't see a bus leaving.

Incidentally, although people complain about buses coming in threes, 'bunching' is actually a natural (if irritating) consequence of the way buses work, and becomes increasingly likely as the buses get further along their route. If one bus gets slightly delayed, the number of people at the next stop increases, slowing it down further so that the buses behind catch up. In real life you are more likely to see buses bunching in twos rather than Mr Blimpton's threes.

19. Tunnel wires *(puzzle, page 19)*

Bob only needs to go to the other end and back once, and he only needs to make two joins of cables.

If we call the four cables A, B, C and D at one end, and 1, 2, 3 and 4 at the other, then Bob first connects A and B together. At the far end he labels the cables 1, 2 , 3 and 4. He then tests until he finds a pair – let's say 2 and 4 – which form a circuit. He now connects one of that pair to another unused cable – say 2 to 3. He then goes back to the other end of the tunnel, disconnects A and B and once again tests until he finds the pair which form a circuit. One of these will be A or B (the other end of 2), the other will be C or D (the other end of 3). Let's suppose the pair is A and C. He now has all the information he needs. In this example:

A is 2, so B is 4, C is 3 and D must be 1.

*Of course, this solution works **whichever** combinations turn out to form the circuits.*

29. Is this the world's simplest game?
(puzzle, page 25)

The trick is very simple – you move onto the long diagonal, from 1 to 2. Your opponent then has to move off the diagonal, allowing you at your second turn to move back onto the diagonal... and all the time you are getting nearer to END, which you will be the first one to occupy, because it is on the long diagonal.

39. Lord Henry's hunt (puzzle, page 31)

Their conversation included two sentences that feature every letter of the alphabet.

"Pack my box with five dozen liquor jugs" does it in 32 letters.

"Quick Baz, get my woven flax jodhpurs" does it in 30, and is perhaps the shortest coherent sentence in the English language that uses all 26 letters.

"A quick brown fox jumped over that lazy dog" is a trick because it contains every letter of the alphabet except 's'. (To include all 26 it should be 'jumps'.) Apologies to readers who jumped to a quick conclusion!

49. By-election blues *(puzzle, page 38)*

There were ten candidates in total.

This can be worked out with a diagram showing the candidates who are happily married and those who weren't involved in the council scandal.

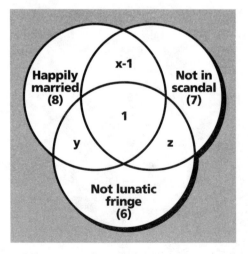

There are X candidates who are happily married and were not involved in the scandal. We know that only one of these X people was not a 'lunatic fringer' (Henrietta Prigg), so the five other non-lunatics must be Y + Z. (If Y + Z added up to more

than 5, then there would be no need for the sixth to be in X either.) So the total number of candidates is 8 + Z (= Y+7). The only numbers that fit are Z = 2, Y = 3, which means there were ten candidates in total.

59. Mum's secret *(puzzle, page 45)*

Mum is 49. Weekends account for two sevenths of her age.

69. A holey poser *(puzzle, page 52)*

The first figure is adapted from a picture from the book Mathematics and the Imagination *by Kasner & Newman. The vertical hole clearly goes through a hole in the horizontal hole.*

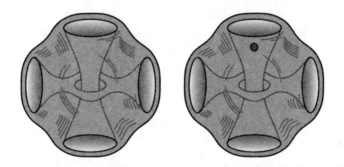

The second figure assumes that the object in the first solution is hollow, as if it were blown from glass, and shows a hole in the hole in the first figure, which goes through a hole in a hole. (There are, of course, alternative ways of picturing these puzzles.)

79. Spot the difference *(puzzle, page 56)*

The cheetah won again. They ran at the same speeds, so that when the leopard had run 90 paces, the cheetah had run 100 and caught up with the leopard. That meant they still had ten

more paces to run to the stream, by which time the cheetah would have nosed ahead.

---

89. Quirky Qwerty *(puzzle, page 64)*

The three longest common words that use letters out of QWERTYUIOP are PROPRIETOR, PERPETUITY and (surprisingly) TYPEWRITER. All three of these words appeared in the puzzle.

---

99. The generation gap *(puzzle, page 69)*

If you count your ancestors back, starting with two parents, four grandparents, eight great-grandparents, 16 great-great grandparents and so on, you clearly have a large number of ancestors who were alive several hundred years ago. In fact, if you count a generation as 30 years, there are about 30 generations in the last 900 years, so you had about 2^{30} ancestors at that time. Since $2^{10} = 2 \times 2 \times 2 \times 2 \times 2 \times 2 \times 2 \times 2 \times 2 \times 2 = 1024$, 2^{30} is more than 1,000,000,000. But the total population of England in Saxon times was only a few million. If you know that your ancestors were not immigrants, then, almost certainly, everyone in those days was an ancestor of yours, and of the professor, many times over
– hence his confidence.

---

10. Menial copying *(puzzle, page 15)*

Eight people (including Brian) went to the meeting.

371 is the product of the number of people Brian invited and the number of pages in each document. The only two numbers which multiplied together give 371 are 7 and 53. So the number of people given documents was either 371, 53 or 7. It is extremely unlikely that Stephanie would have had time to distribute 53 documents to 53 people (let alone 371) in the few minutes available, so by far the most likely answer is that she distributed seven copies of the

document, and each copy had 53 pages in it. Brian kept the original, making eight documents for the eight at the meeting.

20. The tall and the short of it *(puzzle, page 20)*

Yes, it is very likely that it made a difference. Only if the men were arranged in a neat order, getting taller from left to right and back to front, for example, would it make no difference. We can illustrate this with the first figure:

1	2	3	1
4	5	6	4
7	8	9	**7**
7	8	9	

1	2	3	1
7	5	6	**5**
4	8	9	4
7	8	9	

In the array of nine men on the left, whose numbers represent their height in order, the shortest in each row and the tallest in each column have been picked out (in bold), and the tallest shortest and shortest tallest are the same man. In the second figure, however, the fourth and seventh tallest have been switched, and the tallest shortest is now 5 and the shortest tallest is 7.

30. Pub quiz *(puzzle, page 26)*

Including the final there were 18 contests altogether. There is a neat 'lateral' way of solving this. By the end of the competition 36 of the 37 teams must have been knocked out because there is only one winner. One contest knocks out two teams, two contests knock out four teams. As the number of contests must always be half the number of teams knocked out, there must have been 18 contests in total.

There is a slower way of finding the answer. The number of teams in a tournament without byes must be a power of three

125

(three in the final, nine in the semi-finals, 27 in the quarter-finals and so on). So, in the Gussetshire tournament the quarter-finals must have had 27 teams. FIfteen teams must have played in the first round (of whom five got through) to join 22 who had byes, making 27 in the quarter-finals. The total number of contests in each round was:

$5 + 9 + 3 + 1 = 18$

40. Tricky ending *(puzzle, page 32)*

Words such as 'small', 'minimal' or perhaps 'singular' would fit. You cannot write 'one' because then that would mean it occurred twice. 'Once' is incorrect grammar and therefore not allowed.

50. Mate in one *(puzzle, page 39)*

The only possible way of achieving checkmate was if David moved the pawn on b2 to b1 and it became queen. The two brothers were sitting to the left and right of the board as we look at it, so Peter's view was at right angles to the way in which chessboards are normally presented. The key clue to solving this puzzle is that in chess the right-hand square nearest to a player is always white.

60. Switching olives *(puzzle, page 46)*

There are still 100 olives in each dish, so there must be exactly the same number of black olives in the green dish as there are green olives in the black dish.

You do not know how many green olives came back in the mixed handful, but you do know that there was a total of 20. Suppose 17 green and three black olives came across.

	Black dish		Green dish
Start	100B		100G
First swap	80B	20B->	100G, 20B
Second swap	83B,17G	<-17G,3B	83G, 17B

As you can see, at the finish the numbers of green and black in their own dishes are both 83. In fact, this works for any chosen number in the mixture. Some doubters continue to refute this answer. The best way to prove it is to take a real bowl of olives and try it out for yourself.

70. Number anagram *(puzzle, page 52)*

TWO + ELEVEN = THIRTEEN is Nicola's rearranged sum.

TWO + ELEVEN = THREE + TEN is Claire's reshuffle.

80. Set in order *(puzzle, page 57)*

The volumes which he does not move will stay in their original order on the shelf because they are already positioned correctly. All he has to do is to leave as many volumes as possible which are already in ascending order from left to right. The most he can pick out is four, and he can do this in four ways: 3–4–9–10; 3–5–9–10; 3–4–6–8; 3–5–6–8.

It makes no difference which sequence he chooses. He still has to remove and replace each of the remaining six volumes.

(There is a far harder question which does not have a simple solution: since it takes a real effort to push several heavy volumes along the shelf in order to replace the volume he has removed, does it make any difference in which order he removes and replaces these six volumes? The short answer is yes.)

90. The missing marbles *(puzzle, page 64)*

You will get most marbles in all the bags if you put the bags of marbles inside each other. Any way of doing this will increase the number of marbles in the bags, but to get the maximum they should have put all 40 marbles into one bag, and then put that into a second bag, the whole lot into a third bag and finally into a fourth bag. Then it could truly be said that inside each bag were 40 marbles.

100. Shop reflection *(puzzle, page 70)*

The right way round. The easiest way to demonstrate this to yourself is to write on a piece of clear plastic, and look through it at a mirror.

109. Guinness Mindbender *(puzzle, page 76)*

The number that we have in mind is 9,780,851,126,685, and it means Guinness Mindbenders. If you can't see why, tip the cocktail on its side, look at it again and then look at the back of the book.

Although this has been a joint compilation, we have taken responsibility for different puzzles.

Eastaway: 1, 2, 3, 6, 8, 9, 10, 13, 17, 19, 22, 23, 24, 25, 27, 28, 30, 31, 34, 35, 36, 37, 39, 40, 41, 43, 45, 49, 50, 51, 52, 55, 56, 59, 60, 61, 62, 63, 66, 68, 70, 72, 73, 74, 76, 77, 78, 79, 82, 83, 84, 85, 87, 88, 89, 91, 92, 93, 97, 98, 101, 102, 103, 104, 105, 107, 108.

Wells: 4, 5, 7, 12, 14, 15, 16, 18, 20, 21, 26, 29, 32, 33, 38, 42, 44, 46, 47, 48, 53, 54, 57, 67, 69, 75, 77, 80, 81, 86, 90, 94, 95, 96, 99, 100, 106.

Wells/Eastaway: 11, 58, 64, 65, 71, 109.